Praise for Delic

"I absolutely love Rhonda Ryder's ability to bring clarity to the subject of weight and body image in *Delicious Alignment*. I've also been a part of her Facebook group for almost a year where I enjoy the reminders to not only love my body, whatever shape I'm in, but to appreciate whatever I'm inspired to eat. These daily reminders helped me release over 10 pounds without changing anything except my thoughts. Rhonda has helped me close the gap between where I am and where I want to be."
—Danielle Perrino, Family Support Specialist

"These 25 stories are what locks in the inspiration and the 'how-to' on each and every page. It's not just one wise person telling you what to do or what worked, it's an entire cavalry of women sharing how they traded a lifetime of body shame and hate for the freedom to celebrate their food, their bodies and their lives."
—Michelle Spalding, Author of *Glitter, Duct Tape and Magic*

"Employing the Law of Attraction and the importance of managing one's thoughts, Rhonda penetrates the barrier of weight-hate and negative body image by providing five steps and 25 success stories that help one to instill compassion and love for their bodies now and at any size, and inevitably obtain amazing results."
**—Judy Legare, Certified Eating Psychology Coach,
Institute for The Psychology of Eating**

"Since joining Rhonda's Facebook group and reading her book based on the teachings of Abraham-Hicks, I have learned how to love my body and eat foods I enjoy without counting calories or feeling deprived. I have also let go of inches and pounds. I am 63 years old and healthier and happier than I've ever been. I highly recommend *Delicious Alignment* to anyone who is ready for an inner approach that helps you love your body and your entire life!"
—Kim Hussey, Career Advisor

"I LOVE this book! *Delicious Alignment* is full of
encouragement and a step-by-step guide to help you create the body
you want, but more importantly to love your body. It has
given me the tools and the inspiration to not only release pounds, but to
manifest other things in my life. I also got so much out of the stories
which demonstrate how each woman used Abraham teachings to
let go of weight. I can't recommend this book enough.
Everyone should own a copy and share one with a friend!"
—Jennie Winter, Intuitive Healer

"Having studied the Abraham-Hicks perspective for 20 years,
I deeply appreciate Rhonda's bringing Abraham's brilliant,
unique clarity to the subject of weight and body image."
—Karen Money Williams, Author of
It's a Beautiful Day in the Aber-hood

"*Delicious Alignment* addresses an important and seemingly magical
idea, that we can work with our minds to shape our bodies instead
of punishing ourselves into losing weight. As a member of the
Delicious Alignment Facebook group, I can attest to the inspiration,
knowledge and helpfulness of Rhonda Ryder and the women
in the group and in this book. Without them, I'd still be struggling.
Instead, I find my clothes getting bigger and my dreams getting closer.
A fantastic, easy-to-understand volume for getting the self-love
and body you've always wanted."
—Amy Dale, Voice Actress

"*Delicious Alignment* makes clear that sacrifice and struggle
are not absolute prerequisites to physical and spiritual transformation.
Here are 25 women who have proven that to love yourself this very
minute, just exactly as you are, is the first step to any change
you wish to make in your life."
—Robin Wethe Altman, Artist

Delicious Alignment

*How 25 Women Learned to Love and
Transform Their Bodies Using
Abraham-Hicks and the Law of Attraction*

RHONDA RYDER

First paperback edition April 2020

ISBN 978-0-578-65612-0 (paperback)

DeliciousAlignment.com

I dedicate this book to all women (and men) who are learning how to love their bodies, perhaps for the first time in their adult lives.

Contents

PART ONE
The 5 Steps

PART TWO
The 25 Stories

Disclaimer

This book is meant for people who struggle with loving their bodies and their food. Some reading these pages may want to transform their body, while others want to learn how to love and accept their current body—*as is*. I have studied Abraham-Hicks for over 10 years and interviewed 25 women who learned how to love their physical selves after a lifetime of self-criticism and body shame. They also released 25 to 140 pounds each using the spiritual teachings found in Abraham-Hicks and Law of Attraction materials. Everyone reading this book may not want to release pounds. They may simply want to learn how to love their bodies. Having said all that, I am not a weight-loss expert, a physician, an eating disorder specialist or a mental health professional. The information in this book is not meant to be a substitute for medical advice or psychological help. If you are in need of those things, please seek them out.

I am a woman who found herself with a deep desire to understand and share the Law of Attraction-Body Love connection with others who are also seeking the delicious freedom that accompanies self-love.

Who Is Abraham-Hicks?

Abraham is a group of enlightened teachers or a "group consciousness," as it says on the Abraham-Hicks website (abraham-hicks.com), that speaks through Esther Hicks. Esther translates the messages she receives from Abraham to those who are selected to ask questions at Abraham-Hicks workshops around the globe. In 1986, Esther and her late husband, Jerry Hicks, held their first meeting where they allowed a few friends to ask Abraham questions about life, and the rest is history. Abraham-Hicks events and books, etc., began to develop and grow from there, with often sold-out workshops of over 500 attendees.

Introduction

The original title of this book was, *Delicious Alignment: How 25 Women Lost Over 25 Pounds Each Using Abraham-Hicks and the Law of Attraction.* After I started interviewing women about their experiences with Abraham and releasing pounds, I realized the subject of the book was evolving to include how to love your body and your food, no matter what size or shape you are. All of my interviewees released 25 to 140 pounds each, but I didn't want that to be the sole focus of the book anymore. After reading so many other body positivity blogs and books, I realized that focusing solely on releasing pounds would contribute to the diet mentality we're all trying to ditch. (You'll notice I try to use the words "release pounds" as opposed to "lose weight" in Part One because if you "lose" something, that usually means you want to "find" it again. When you "release" something, you let it go.)

Further, during the course of the interviews, each woman spoke more about the freedom she attained from learning how to love her body and her food than the weight she released. (Not that there's anything wrong with wanting to make changes to your body. As we'll discuss later, whether you want to tone up, gain or release pounds, or love the skin you're in, it's your body and your preferences.)

I must confess I initially began this project because *I wanted to release pounds*. And not only did I want to release pounds, I wanted to release pounds using the teachings of Abraham-Hicks and the Law of Attraction (they are one-and-the-same-to-me) because I believed it to be the only way I could succeed long term. So I thought if I interviewed women who had been successful using these teachings to manifest their desired body, I could "crack the code" so to speak and finally release the pounds myself. Once I cracked the code, I could then share this message with others who could benefit as well.

I felt this approach was pretty much my last resort. In the past 14 years, I had worked with various weight-loss coaches. I had completed nutritional programs with holistic doctors after experiencing digestive issues and having my gall bladder removed. It was all to no avail. You see, the other times I've released pounds (when I was single), I always had an outside motivator. I wanted to attract a handsome man to date, and that reason alone seemed to provide the necessary motivation to exercise like a hamster on a treadmill after two cups of coffee and pass up those late-night ice cream binges. Today I know better than to look for motivation outside myself. After all, *I'm spiritual*. It's about inspiration, not motivation. And I'm obsessed with Abraham-Hicks. I've been studying and listening to these teachings for over 10 years. I attended an Abraham discussion group in Florida for seven of those years, and I lead an Abraham-Hicks discussion group here in Asheville, North Carolina.

After realizing the importance of accepting my body before I could manifest long-term changes, I began a new journey toward self-love. I started focusing on the things I appreciated about my body, and amazing things started happening. I began exercising, drinking more water and eating healthier. These actions were inspired—not forced (a huge difference). That's just one of the reasons I'm so excited you have this book in your hands. I want to share this message with as many women (and men) who are open to these teachings as I possibly can. There's a lot of freedom offered in these pages around body image, and it's time for all of us to claim that freedom for ourselves.

Here's What This Book Is Not About

As you might have surmised by now, this is not a diet book. It's also not a book about how to get "the perfect body." It's not about trying to reach a beauty or fitness standard someone else created. It's about what *you* want for yourself and your body, whether that's learning to love your current body while releasing pounds or learning to love and accept where you are—period. (If what you do want is to release pounds, you have the opportunity to learn from the 25 stories and the five steps in this book.) In addition, you won't find any recipes, food plans or nutrition information. Nor will you find any eating styles except for the ones mentioned in the personal stories. We won't spend any time on what to eat, when to eat, how to eat or where to eat it.

That's because each woman I interviewed—when she applied what she knew about the Law of Attraction to her body transformation desires—was guided to the food plan or the eating style that was right for her. Each woman learned how to listen to her own Inner Guidance and trust the messages she received about food. So an eating style that works for one person doesn't necessarily work for another. It's a totally intuitive and individual thing.

What This Book Is About

As I mentioned, I interviewed over 25 women about how they learned to love and transform their bodies using the teachings of Abraham-Hicks and the Law of Attraction. At the end of every interview, I asked each woman to share five steps she recommends for any like-minded person who also wants to learn how to love, or love *and* transform, her body. You will find their stories and their steps in Part Two of this book.

I then consolidated the various steps given by all the interviewees into the five steps outlined in Part One. What you're about to read is not theory. *It's actually how they did it.* These five steps are *their five steps.* Although the interviewees may have used different words to describe their journey to body acceptance and transformation, I discovered their steps are virtually the same. One person might have emphasized one step over another, and they might have put the steps in different order, but at the end of the day, they were basically all saying the same thing (which was quite an exciting discovery, to say the least).

Since beginning this book project, I have heard from hundreds of women in my online group and course who have also experienced learning how to love themselves and their bodies as well as those who have created the changes in their bodies they desired. This is all thrilling to me, and I hope it is to you, too. It means this approach is working for countless others, and if it's working for them, it can work for you.

As for me, you can read my story in the following pages where I share how conducting the interviews and writing this book have not only helped me release pounds, but more importantly, helped me stop the vicious cycle of obsessing over food and weight.

My hope is that this book inspires you to connect with your Inner Being (I'll talk more about your Inner Being in Step 1) in an even deeper way so you, too, can find the beauty and the wholeness of your spiritual and physical self—in the now.

How to Use This Book

This book is separated into two parts. Part One describes the five steps to learning how to love, or love and transform, your body. These steps were derived from the interviews I conducted with 25 women, women who released 25 to 140 pounds by studying and applying the teachings of Abraham-Hicks and the Law of Attraction.

These steps are not linear in nature, meaning you don't have to fully complete one step before moving onto the next. The five steps are fluid and often overlap one another. Understanding and implementing these steps is more a way of life than a one-time application. Consistent practice of these steps is the best approach *(rather than seeking to do any one step perfectly)*.

You can either read the steps first or mix it up and read a step, followed by a few of the stories. The stories help to demonstrate how the interviewees integrated these steps into their lives. While each story is unique, you will find the steps they embarked upon are similar.

I highly recommend reading the book in its entirety. Each step is a vital part of the process, and each story will inspire you through the actual results these women achieved and how they did it.

Each Woman Includes Five of Her Own Steps

As I mentioned above, each woman interviewed in Part Two also gives five of her own recommended steps to loving, or loving and transforming, your body. I asked each woman to share her own five steps in order to see if there was a pattern emerging with all 25 women.

And there was. The five steps I've put together are the culmination of what these women shared with me and what I learned from Abraham.

I include each woman's five steps at the end of her interview not to confuse you but to give you multiple ways to hear the same information. We are all different. We have different communication styles, different preferences. Therefore, you have 25 opportunities to find what resonates with you. By reading these stories, you can pick and choose what you are drawn to, what inspires you and what you want to incorporate into your life.

Love Notes and Quote Bubbles

In Part One you will find Love Notes at the end of each step and Quote Bubbles sprinkled throughout. Each contains comments made by women (and a few men) in my Delicious Alignment Facebook group and page. Hopefully, these comments further add clarity to the benefits of learning how to love your body and your food. Names have been changed to protect people's privacy.

Exercises at the End of Each Step

You will find Love Your Body Exercises *(these are mindset/spiritual exercises)* at the end of each step. I highly recommend purchasing a journal so you can have unlimited space to write about your insights and do the exercise work. Many of your breakthroughs will happen from these writings. However, if you're not much of a writer, do not despair. The important thing is to absorb the material and the exercises in the way that is best for you *(the path of least resistance, as Abraham says)*.

Resources

There are many more resources I wish to share with you to support you on your journey to loving your body, your food and your life. You can find these on my Resources page at DeliciousAlignment.com. There you can keep informed of what I'm up to and connect with like-minded people on social media as well as learn about any coaching and online programs offered at the time. Enjoy!

My Story

This is my story, and I believe it is just that: "a story," like anything else we tell ourselves. So why focus on the "gory" details? I want to give you insight into the journey I've traveled with this physical body up to now. I want to paint a picture of how Abraham-Hicks and the Law of Attraction helped me not only release pounds but gain the freedom to finally discover how to love and appreciate my body.

If you would have told me five years ago I would write a book about how to love, or love and transform, your body based on the Law of Attraction and the teachings of Abraham-Hicks, I would have said you were crazy. I am the last person anyone would come to for health and fitness advice. Why? Because I've been struggling with food and weight since I was 15. I've been obsessed with my size and full of shame and guilt about being "overweight" much of my life. I once reached 213 pounds (that was my highest), and I'm 5'3". While I've since learned to love myself and my body no matter what size I am, for most of my life, my size and shape defined my worthiness.

I've often wondered why I started gaining weight at 15. I do remember often feeling sad. Even depressed. My dad experienced depression, and he was also an alcoholic. My mom, although fun and loving, had a hot temper.

The fighting between my parents (they were very young when they had my sister and me) was the thing that upset me the most. I'm sure I turned to food as a way to escape as I got a little older. Food and TV. I wanted to feel better, so that's how I learned to survive. Shut it all out. Go numb.

As the time I spent in front of the TV grew, so did the amount of junk food I ate. A two-day TV and eating binge grew into week-long and even month-long binges. Nobody saw me eating like that except my mom. Not my friends, not my boyfriend, no one. My mother would buy me the food after I'd given her a list of ice cream, cookies and candy bars. I could eat all the items on the list in one evening.

When I was about 17, I remember thinking, "Doesn't anyone see what I'm doing to myself? Does anyone care? Does anyone notice I'm depressed?" I was upstairs one day and felt that I was about to lose my mind. Crying, I begged my father to pay for me to go to a therapist. "I can't stop eating," I cried. The poor guy didn't know what to do. He couldn't understand my problem because he couldn't relate. He was always thin. He replied, "Just stop eating!" Well, if I could do that, I wouldn't be having this conversation, I thought. I was devastated. I really needed help.

Throughout college, I tried Overeaters Anonymous. I tried Weight Watchers. I tried diet pills. I bought stacks of nutrition and diet books, although I barely read any of them. At times, I would exercise excessively, thinking that the only way anyone would want to date me was if I looked different. Basically nothing worked long term. I always returned to compulsive TV watching accompanied by compulsive binge-eating followed by extreme self-loathing. Something would trigger me and I would seek to escape once again.

I knew I had to do something. Thinking a change of scenery would help, I decided to take a break from college and move to Colorado. A friend was living there and had invited me to be her roommate. While in Colorado, I made many friends, but I never dated. My self-esteem in the dating arena was still at an all-time low due to my weight.

Six months later, I moved back to New York City and back in with my parents to finish my degree. After graduating, I entered the workplace in Manhattan in a large advertising agency. While I loved advertising, I didn't like the rat race of the city, so after two years of getting packed into subways like a sardine just to get to work, I moved to Kissimmee, Florida, to focus on my writing. This turned out to be a very good move for me. Happier there on my own, I started exercising more and releasing pounds. My food and TV binges were still a part of life, but I was able to keep my weight somewhat under control, even though I was never totally satisfied with my appearance.

Florida became my home. When I was 30 years old, I was working at Walt Disney World and met a special person there. We dated for two years and had a baby. We were planning to get married, but I called it off. It was for the best because we fought a lot. I didn't want to raise my son in the same kind of toxic environment that I experienced as a child.

I loved being a mom and loved my son more than anything in the world. It was the best thing that ever happened to me. And for some reason, I was able to release more weight a few months after giving birth. I was looking gooooood. How did I do it? Well, I remember saying a particular mantra a million times a day: "I am fit and beautiful and everybody loves me." And it worked! I made healthier food choices (choices that were in alignment with my beliefs about releasing pounds.

We'll talk about the role beliefs play in releasing pounds in Step 3). I also continued working out, toning up and feeling sexy and beautiful.

The mantra worked because I chose to focus on the *future me* in terms of what I wanted to look like instead of the *current me*, while at the same time accepting and loving the current me. I continued repeating that mantra and holding that vision in my mind. I chose to focus on what I wanted, which was a smaller, fit body. I avoided mirrors and kept focusing on seeing myself as fit and beautiful. Hovering at a size 10-12 for about four years, I felt pretty good, although I always wanted to be smaller. Still, I was grateful to feel sexy and attractive again. I dated, socialized and enjoyed life.

In 1993, when my son was nearly a year old, a friend told me about Landmark Education (a company offering personal development courses), and I participated in nearly every program and seminar they offered during the next 12 years. I healed many long-term hurts and made lifetime friends at Landmark Education, friends I still have today. About four years later, I married and had another child, although my marriage was a very short one. In retrospect, I rushed into that commitment because I wanted so badly for my son to have a father figure.

After the divorce, I managed to vacillate between a size 12 and 14. After single-parenting for seven years, enjoying my life and my children, I met my second husband, Steven, and began to experience the healthiest romantic relationship I've ever had. He helped me raise my two children, and I often call him a saint because he is the sweetest, kindest man I've ever known.

Over the 14 plus years of our marriage, I gained back the pounds I released and more. In order to avoid feeling upset, I never stepped on the scale (though I could tell I gained weight because I couldn't fit into my clothes). The bottom line: I was still obsessed with my weight.

Thankfully, since the age of 17, spirituality played an important part in my life. I loved metaphysics. My introduction to the Law of Attraction was the book *Sermon on the Mount* by Emmet Fox, where I first heard the concept that our thoughts create our reality. I discovered Abraham-Hicks around 2008 and completely fell in love with these teachings, as I've mentioned. I've been following Abraham for more than 10 years now, previously attending meetings every month that my dear friend and Law of Attraction author, Karen Money Williams (karenmoneywilliams.com), and her partner, Mark Toms, lead in Winter Springs, Florida. Steven and I, along with my dad, eventually moved to North Carolina where I started my own Abraham-Hicks discussion group.

I've had this idea for a while to write a book about releasing pounds using the teachings of Abraham and the Law of Attraction. As I said in the Introduction, the concept of this book ultimately morphed into learning how to love yourself and your body no matter what size you are, while creating change (if that's something you want). My Inner Being nudged me to write this book for three years before I dared to start. I kept suppressing the idea because *I wasn't as thin as I thought I should be to write it.*

After my husband, dad and I were well established in Asheville, the idea for the book pestered me (believe me, I tried to make it disappear). Finally, in January 2018, I said yes. I took a leap of faith and trusted my guidance, even though the thought of writing and publishing this book scared the heck out of me at times. The message I kept hearing from within was persistent, and I have to say, I'm so glad I finally listened. One thing after another fell into place.

As I began to interview women who learned how to love their bodies, released pounds and went down multiple clothes sizes using Abraham-Hicks and the Law of Attraction, I felt delighted and energized. One by one, they revealed the underlying purpose of this book: learn how to love and accept yourself and your body. Whether your ultimate goal is to transform your body or find happiness where you are, you first must learn how to love the skin you're in.

I may not be the diet industry's version of fit,
but I'm my version of happy.

At the time of publishing this book, I have gone down three clothing sizes and released over 25 pounds and counting. My desire is to reach a size 12 (I am currently a size 14). I'm so excited that I'm almost there. For me, part of loving my body includes listening to what it likes to do for fun and for health. My body, and definitely my soul, love hiking the beautiful mountains that surround us here in Asheville, North Carolina. My body also loves Pilates and working out with weights. I like learning how to cook delicious meals (or better yet, enjoying the "farm to table" restaurants Asheville is known for). Also, I no longer suffer from shame and guilt if my weight fluctuates or if I indulge in certain foods I used to consider "bad." I have a much healthier relationship with food and my body now. I may not be the diet industry's version of fit, but I'm my version of happy.

And the best part? I now coach others how to love their bodies and their lives. This book and the resulting coaching work are nothing short of a labor of love. I often feel this is what I came here to do: help women learn how to love and accept their bodies in the present moment. Once you begin doing that, you can start manifesting the body and life you truly desire

PART ONE
The 5 Steps

Step 1

Get Off the Scale and Get in Alignment

You become that which you believe you can become.
~Bhagavad Gita, Sanskrit Scripture

I f you're a student of Abraham-Hicks, you know the premise of their teachings is based on the Law of Attraction and getting in alignment. Alignment is pretty much the solution to everything. If you want a better relationship, get in alignment. If you want more money, get in alignment. If you want to manifest the body you desire, get in alignment.

If you could take one thing with you after reading this book, it would be the concept of alignment.

What Exactly Does Getting in Alignment Mean and How Can It Help You Create the Body You Desire?

To put it simply, thinking thoughts that cause you to feel emotionally good means you're in alignment. Conversely, mentally focusing in ways that lead you to feel emotionally bad means you're out of alignment. It's not feasible to be in alignment 100% of the time, so it's important to be easy on yourself when you experience "resistance," meaning unhappy thoughts that lead to unhappy feelings such as a sense of struggle or disappointment.

There's a huge up-side to experiencing resistance. When you're feeling negative and upset, you become very clear about what you don't want. This is actually good news. Knowing what you don't want helps you know what you DO want. In other words, your negative emotions help you clarify your desires. However, after you've noticed the negative emotions, it's best to get back into alignment by finding happier thoughts as soon as possible because that's how you allow what you want to flow into your life, including the body you would like to manifest. That's how you *attract* the things you really want.

By the way, despite the title of this step, if hopping on the scale gets you in alignment, go for it. As you proceed through the pages of this book, you'll realize it's all about what works for *you*. It's also about learning to trust the guidance you receive from your Inner Being.

It Works Because You're Aligning with Your Inner Being

Your Inner Being is guiding you every moment. *Who or what is your Inner Being?* That is for you to decide. Some people think of their Inner Being as God or their Higher Power. Some people think of their Inner Being as the Universe or their soul. For me, I'm not sure what "it" is. Sometimes I think of my Inner Being as an energy or the Universe, but I don't have a visual. I was raised Catholic, but I certainly don't see a male figure sitting on a throne in the heavens when I think of my Inner Being. However, I do know when I take the time to sit in silence, focus within myself and connect with my Inner Being, I am more relaxed and confident. I may not know what to do next, but I believe I will eventually receive guidance. I know that seeking a deeper relationship with my Inner Being is the best possible thing I can do for myself.

When you feel emotionally good, you are in alignment with your Inner Being; you are viewing things in the same joyful way your Inner Being does. You can always tell if you are viewing things in that way by how you feel emotionally. Feeling good? Then you are aligning with your Inner Being. Not feeling good? Then you're not. It really is that simple.

See Yourself as Your Inner Being Sees You

If you're beating yourself up because you ate two (or six) chocolate cupcakes or because you had a hard time fitting into the "made for size five females" airplane seat, you're not seeing yourself the way your Inner Being sees you. Your Inner Being sees you as beautiful. Period. End of story. Your job is to line up with that kind of love for yourself, or at least move toward it. (In Step 2, we'll talk about how to start a love affair with your body.)

When we are feeling bad about our bodies, our food choices or our behavior, we also feel disconnected: disconnected from others, disconnected from ourselves and disconnected from our Inner Being.

While this separation is an illusion (we are never really disconnected from ourselves, our Inner Being or others), we feel it nonetheless. But the real questions to ask when we're criticizing ourselves are...

What Would My Inner Being Say?

- Would my Inner Being agree I'm a failure?
- Would my Inner Being agree I'm further away from my goals and dreams than ever?
- Would my Inner Being agree I'm unattractive?

The answer is no.

Your Inner Being would not agree with these things. Not one bit, because your Inner Being loves you. Your Inner Being sees only the good in you. Your Inner Being sees your light, your beauty and your perfection.

> I appreciate my body in every aspect. I ask my Inner Being to direct me to the best food for my body in any given moment. I see myself at my perfect weight. I've lost 12 pounds without putting any food on the "bad" list. I'm focused on the feeling of health and it's working.
> **—Angie**

I remember hearing Abraham say, "Your Inner Being absolutely adores you, and the connection with your Inner Being is more valuable to you and feels better to you than if every person on this planet from their physical perspective said 'I love you' at one time."

Now that's what I call a whole lotta love!

The Universe is not discriminating about the rightness or the wrongness of your request. It is here to accommodate all requests. All you have to do is be a vibrational match to your request, and the Universe will yield it to you.

~Abraham-Hicks, excerpted from Sacramento, CA 5/13/00

The Law of Attraction Always Says Yes

Whether you're thinking about what you want or thinking about what you *don't want*, the Law of Attraction says yes to it all.

In other words, the Law of Attraction brings you what you're thinking about. So if you're thinking about how much you hate your size, the Law of Attraction will bring you more experiences of being unhappy with your size.

How our thoughts create reality makes sense to me when I look at my own life. Growing up as a pre-teen, teenager and young adult, I focused on how much I resented myself for overeating and gaining weight. This kind of thinking only led me to attract more of the same: gaining weight.

I also focused on wanting to lose weight. I was obsessed with it. So what did I create? More experiences of wanting to lose weight, "wanting" being the key word. I lived in a perpetual state of wanting.

There is nothing wrong with wanting. Abraham describes wanting as part of the creation process. It's how we identify new desires. But once we have identified the new desire, we need to, at some point, move past the wanting phase and enter the allowing phase so we can experience the manifestation.

How Does Alignment Work?

Think of a garden hose with the water spurting out representing all the things you want to experience. When you're in alignment, it's like you've opened the faucet and all your good can flow right into the container called your life.

You attract more of what you want when you're in alignment because you're an open vessel, ready to receive. When you're not in alignment (when you're feeling fear, for example), it's as if you've turned off the faucet or put a kink in the hose, temporarily disallowing the things you want to manifest.

Don't worry; you can never really cut off your good because it's all there for you, waiting for you to *allow* it into your experience. When you're not in alignment, you simply keep the things and the relationships you want at arm's length. You keep what you want from manifesting into your physical experience, including the transformation of your physical body.

Altering behavior about food without tending to your vibration nets minimal results, while altering thought will yield great returns without the necessity of altering the behavior.

~Esther and Jerry Hicks, authors of
Money, and the Law of Attraction

Good Vibrations

Everyone has a vibration or frequency they emit. "Good vibrations" is more than a cute saying or a famous Beach Boys song. It's a real phenomenon that affects your entire life. Have you ever met someone and immediately felt a good vibe from them? We all have. You can certainly tell if you are drawn to a person or not, almost immediately, even before they open their mouth. You, too, have a vibration. Your vibration is dynamic and ever-varying to match the essence of your present mental focus.

Managing your vibration via managing your thoughts and resulting emotions is how you get into alignment. If you're upset, you're in a lower vibration. If you're feeling appreciation, you're in a much higher vibration. Your vibration determines your alignment. Your vibration also determines other things.

One woman I interviewed shared how she could eat the same number of calories and expend the same amount of physical activity in a week (she tracked it), and if her vibration was low, meaning she was not in alignment that week, she wouldn't release any pounds. However, if her vibration was higher, meaning she was happier and feeling good, she would release pounds. (We'll talk more about the connection between your vibrational frequency and your metabolism in Step 4.)

Go Easy on Yourself

It doesn't mean you're doing something wrong if you're at a lower vibration (out of alignment) or if you haven't manifested what you want in terms of your body or anything else you desire at this time. Abraham says you can never get it wrong and you never get it done. All that means is you haven't lined up your vibration with the thing you want—yet. When you are at, or near, the same vibrational frequency as what you want, it must come to you. It is law.

If you want to find the secrets of the universe, think in terms of energy, frequency and vibration.

~Nikola Tesla, inventor and scientist

When You're in Alignment, You're at a Higher Vibration

It is simply amazing to me how all the women I interviewed for this book, though their stories may be different, came to similar realizations before and during the transformations of their bodies. They all shared, in different words, how alignment allowed them to begin to open the door to manifesting not only the relationship with food they wanted but the body they desired. They realized if they were going to achieve success with creating the body they wanted, they were going to have to learn how to maintain a good-feeling vibration—in other words, get in alignment more often.

Although I generally understood the importance of a good-feeling vibration, it really clicked for me when writing this book and hearing the stories of all the women who had what I wanted: body love and acceptance and a healthy relationship with food. I finally began to understand that in order to successfully transform my body, I was going to have to stop indulging in my bouts of "poor me's." *I was literally going to have to become a happier person.* I became more serious (or less serious?) about having fun. I became more intentional about visualization and meditation. (We'll talk more about visualization and meditation in Steps Three and Five.) I became...well, more aligned.

Alignment comes from YOU. Not someone else. Not a program. Not a teacher. YOU are your teacher. YOU are your Source. YOU are your Inner Being. Everything in this book leads you to one place: your relationship with your true self.

During the past week, I noticed how my jeans were getting loose. I really didn't think anything of it until it dawned on me that I might have released some pounds or inches. This morning I stayed positive and tried on a smaller size pants and they fit perfectly. The exciting part is I didn't stop eating my favorite foods. I didn't start exercising. I just accepted myself for the amazing person I am and let it go. I'm going to milk this for all it's worth!

—Kit

How to Get in Alignment

There are many ways to get in alignment. The trick is to find what works best for you. Different techniques may be more effective at different times. It's helpful to have a toolbox to select from when your vibration has dipped a little lower than you'd like.

Alignment Booster

I have a special PDF (print out) for you called *The 10 Alignment Boosters*. These 10 ideas will help you get into alignment. You can get the PDF, print it out and hang it in your office or kitchen by going to my Resources page on my website at DeliciousAlignment.com. It's a helpful reminder to get in alignment and raise your vibration any time you are feeling out of sorts.

The following are a few alignment techniques you can experiment with to see what works best for you.

What Would Make Me Feel Better Right Now?

The first thing to do when feeling out of alignment is to ask yourself, "What would make me feel better right now?"

Maybe it's a nature walk. Maybe it's taking five minutes to quiet your mind and breathe deeply. Maybe it's journaling or listening to an Abraham-Hicks video. Maybe it's calling a friend. If you're at work, maybe it's simply thinking a better-feeling thought or taking a break.

It is our promise to you—if you write things you appreciate in others, in life and in yourself, you will have such a dramatic change in thirty days and if continued for six months, the change will be so powerful, so strong, that others who know you will not recognize the old you.

~Neville Goddard, prophet and author

Write an Appreciation List

Appreciation is one of the fastest ways to raise your vibration. In fact, we will talk about appreciation many times in this book. The vibration of appreciation is way up there on Abraham-Hicks' Emotional Guidance Scale along with joy, freedom, love and feeling empowered. (The Emotional Guidance Scale, as explained by Abraham in the book *Ask and It Is Given* is a scale of emotions from the highest vibration to the lowest.)

When I need an alignment boost, I often sit down and write 20 things I appreciate. In fact, the power of appreciation improved my life so much that I decided to add it to my daily routine. Every morning (or most mornings), I meditate for 15 minutes, visualize for five or 10 minutes and then write a list of 20 things I appreciate in my journal.

I start by appreciating my experiences of the previous day. If I'm in a low vibration, writing this list always makes me feel better. If I'm feeling great to begin with, it raises my vibration even more.

What if You Can't Think of Anything to Appreciate?

I have experienced being in such a low vibration that I could hardly think of anything to appreciate. That's why I love this technique. It taught me that during those lower vibration times, I could appreciate basic things like the roof over my head, access to food and water or the air I breathe.

In fact, I have completely turned my day around by taking a few minutes to jot down what I appreciate. If pen and paper aren't available, you can type notes on your phone. If you're driving, you can simply make a mental list and perhaps write it down later. (If you really don't feel inclined to make the list at that particular time, don't force it. It's always best to follow your Inner Guidance and wait until it feels right.) Appreciation is magic. It will work literal miracles in your life, so definitely give it a try.

Scientists have recently determined that it takes approximately 400 repetitions to create a new synapse in the brain—unless it is done with play, in which case, it takes between 10-20 repetitions.

~Dr. Karyn Purvis, founder of the
TCU Institute of Child Development

Do Something Fun

There was a period when I was working on this book that I sequestered myself in the house for almost a month, forcing myself to write. I didn't make plans with friends or with my husband. I didn't allow myself to have fun. I had a book to write and this is the way I would get it done (I thought).

I quickly learned that ignoring my Inner Guidance was not a good idea. It wasn't a good idea when it came to relationships, food and self-love, and it wasn't a good idea when it came to writing a book. Sure, there were times when the writing was flowing and it felt good to keep going. There were other times when I yearned to be around people, to socialize, to laugh, to dance...to let loose. I found when I ignored the guidance I received to go out and take a break, the writing not only suffered, it stalled.

Never underestimate the importance of fun and play. If you observe some of the happiest people around, you will find they have two things in common: 1) a sense of appreciation and 2) a sense of humor. In other words, they are thankful and playful.

Fun means different things to different people. You get to define what fun and play mean to you. When we deprive ourselves of the fun we are craving, we feel disconnected from our Inner Being and we look for ways to fill that void, but only our connection with our Inner Being can satisfy that need.

Listening to your guidance by paying attention to your emotions will help you experience more joy. More joy will help you appreciate yourself and your life more. It will help you experience alignment on a more consistent basis. And since alignment is the key to everything you want, including the relationship with your body you desire, fun and play are definitely worth pursuing, especially if you catch yourself being overly serious and regimented.

There are many other techniques we'll address throughout this book to help you get into alignment. In addition, the previously mentioned book, *Ask and It Is Given* by Esther and Jerry Hicks, is well-known for its many processes that help raise your vibration.

In the next step, we are going to dig deeper into the subject of learning how to love yourself and your current body, a vital part of the formula for manifesting the body you desire or finding contentment in the one you have.

Love Notes

Sharon Everything became so much easier when I put alignment first!

Karen I spent my whole adult life counting calories, measuring my food and exercising like a nut. I still exercise, but now everything is about how I feel. That's the most important thing.

Lucy Whenever I start criticizing the way I look, I now catch myself and ask my Inner Being, "How do you see me? I want to see myself through your eyes." This works because my Inner Being always sees me as beautiful.

Kerry I practice connecting with my body, being in alignment and forgiving myself and others. My focus has shifted from losing weight to feeling good.

Nancy I ate chocolate cake today and I did not feel guilty. It's the guilt that's the problem, not the cake!

Susan When I think, "I shouldn't eat this or that," I know I'm charging my food with negative energy. I've stopped doing that.

Mary My life does not revolve around food anymore. It revolves around doing whatever I need to do to get in alignment. Then everything else falls into place.

Judy I've been guided to eat what I consider healthier foods since I've made feeling good my number one priority.

Bonnie My body knows what to do with the food I choose to eat.

Sara I stopped focusing on my weight and boom, it happened because I stopped the resistance. I did nothing—no exercise, no diet. I'm at the weight I wanted for three years now.

Love Your Body Exercises

LOVE YOUR BODY EXERCISE #1.1

Make Your Alignment a Priority

Throughout your day, be aware of your alignment.

How do you know if you're in alignment? If you're feeling good, you're in alignment. If you're not, you're out of alignment.

Ask yourself: Am I feeling good? Am I feeling stressed? Am I happy, unhappy?

If you're feeling frustrated *(or any other negative emotion),* ask yourself, "What can I think or do to get back in alignment?" And do it. When you focus on alignment as best you can, you get better and better at self-, food- and body-love. Remember, it's a process. Be gentle with yourself as you begin to practice making "how you feel" a priority.

SUGGESTION: Purchase a notebook or a special journal to dedicate solely for all the exercises in this book.

ANSWER THE FOLLOWING IN YOUR JOURNAL:

1. *Is there anything you are frustrated or stressed about right now?*
2. *What are a few things you can do right now that would make you feel better?*
3. *What thoughts can you think right now that feel better to you?*

When you look out into the environment that surrounds you and you feel appreciation for what you see, you tune yourself to the frequencies of the best of all that you are. And then, the best of all-that-is, is all that you will see. That is how you manage your point of attraction.

~Abraham-Hicks, excerpted from Boca Raton, FL
1/18/14

LOVE YOUR BODY EXERCISE #1.2

Write an Appreciation List

Write a list of 10 to 20 aspects of your life you appreciate. Even better, incorporate your Appreciation List into your morning routine. You will be amazed at how good you will feel after writing your Appreciation List.

Step 2
Start a Love Affair with Your Body

If you're inspired by me that's wonderful, I'm glad, but I hope it's because
I'm a woman who learned to love herself no matter what size she is.
~Whitney Way Thore, star of *My Big Fat Fabulous Life*

Almost every woman I interviewed for this book shared that one of the first steps to manifesting the body you desire is accepting and loving your current body. This idea of loving and accepting your current body may seem like an impossible task, depending on where you are on your journey. I remember so many times, especially after a food binge or eating something I thought I shouldn't, I would engage in self-criticism for days, weeks or even months. It would take me awhile to get to a place where I could feel good about myself and my body again. The best thing to do is begin where you are and move toward self-love and self-acceptance from there.

All my adult life, I kept thinking I needed to be a certain size in order to feel okay about myself—in order to fit in. In order to be good enough.

Well, what if I am good enough right now...at any size? What if I am good enough *as is*?

The answer is of course, we are all good enough right now, without changing a single muscle group. But how do we internalize that truth? How do we embrace ourselves in the now? These steps, and the 25 stories to follow, give you a starting point with which to jumpstart your self-acceptance and eventual self-love. Whether you want to stay at your current weight or chisel your body into something different that pleases you, it doesn't matter. What matters most is that you love and accept yourself. That is where true freedom lies.

Decide today to have a sort of love affair with your own body. You have to come into utter appreciation, actual love of yourself.

~Abraham-Hicks, excerpted from Asheville, NC 10/29/00

How Do You Learn to Love and Accept Your Current Body While, at the Same Time, Focusing on the Body You Want to Manifest?

It's no fun criticizing yourself. It's no fun feeling like you're getting further and further away from your goals. It's no fun adding a side of guilt to almost everything you eat. For many of us, we've become so good at criticizing ourselves that we can't imagine doing anything differently.

I've listened to countless audios of Abraham talking about how it's important to love and accept your current body before you can manifest your dream body. But how do you do both at the same time? How do you love and accept where you are while visualizing something different?

When you think about it, it makes perfect sense. If you're unhappy about your current body, then that's the vibration you're putting out to the Universe: unhappiness about your body. As a result, you can only attract more of the same: more unhappiness about your body.

When you begin the practice of finding things you *appreciate* about your body, you will attract more complimentary thoughts, and they will begin to multiply rapidly, bringing you more of what you want instead of what you don't want. These new thoughts set the stage for you to manifest the body you truly desire.

Through studying Abraham-Hicks and the Law of Attraction, I've learned it doesn't have to take long to love and accept your current body. You can embark upon soothing yourself with better-feeling thoughts right now.

I'm not going to apologize for my size. I'm not wrong for having the body that I do. I still deserve to dress cool. I still deserve to feel as glamorous or as "Hollywood cool" as anyone else.

~Aidy Bryant, performer on *Saturday Night Live*

Happy Where You Are and Eager for More

In July 2017, I hired an Abraham-Hicks Weight Loss coach named Diana (I'll tell you more about how I found Diana in a minute). She was an integral part of my journey in learning how to release guilt around food, weight and family drama going on in my life at the time. She told me of her experience in the hot seat at an Abraham-Hicks workshop. (At workshops, Abraham calls volunteers from the audience to sit in a chair in the front of the room. These volunteers can then ask Abraham questions.) Diana took advantage of her time in the hot seat to inquire, "If there was one message I could bring back to my Facebook group about food and weight, what would it be?" Abraham answered, "Be happy where you are and eager for more."

Happy where you are, in the context of your body (or anything in your life), means accepting where you are. It seems like a paradox that you need to accept and love yourself where you are before you can manifest something different, but that's the way Law of Attraction works. Until you're reasonably happy, you can't match up with your happy desires.

We think we'll be happy when we have more money, release the pounds or find the hot guy or girl who will fall in love with our quirks. However, it's the getting happy first that attracts the things we want.

When I began writing this book and focusing on loving myself and my body, I was delighted with opportunities that started coming my way—opportunities that had nothing to do with my BMI. One was an invitation to sing on stage at the Center for Spiritual Living here in Asheville. All my life, I fantasized about singing in public but never dared take the leap. My parents always stayed painfully silent when I sang, and my kids made fun of me whenever I belted out "Bohemian Rhapsody" in the car. In their defense, my voice definitely has a limited range. Still, I loved to sing and at times thought I didn't sound half-bad. I finally got up the courage to join the band at the Center for Spiritual Living Asheville and a few months later, I was asked to sing my first solo, "What a Wonderful World," to an enthusiastic audience of over 150 attendees. Two months after that, I received the inspiration to write the lyrics and melody to a song about the Law of Attraction and how we create our own reality with our thoughts (very Abraham). I recorded myself singing it and sent it to the music director at the Center. He generously offered to get the music down on paper (I have no idea how to write music) and coach me on the delivery and arrangement. I sang that song at the Center recently. Numerous people told me how they were moved to tears by the song and by my performance. I always knew I could move people emotionally with my writing—but with my singing? That was a big surprise. The added bonus to my new singing hobby? The daily rehearsing of uplifting, positive music in my car and bathroom turned out to be a powerful meditation for me and put me in a higher vibration every time.

On the next page are the lyrics to the song I wrote and performed.

"What's It Gonna Be"
© Rhonda Ryder

Have you heard the news today?
There's another sunny day, for you
It's true

Have you heard the news today?
The lilies will bloom in May, for you
It's true

I don't need to be updated
About the news that's overrated
My TV and WIFI are unplugged
Today

I don't need to be informed
Of all the things that have gone wrong
I create a world that's good to me

So what's it gonna be?
Are you gonna live your life in fear?
Or are you gonna go inside and hear?
The truth that breathes in you

Are you gonna listen to the hate?
Or are you gonna know a better fate?
That love is all there is

They say my head is in the sand
And if we're silent we'll be damned
But I know love.....has...a plan

It's a choice you get to make now
Focus on the world you want now
See the world you wanna see
So what's it gonna be?

The other opportunity came when a friend asked me to submit a 10-minute play for a Playwriting Festival she was producing. That led to an invitation to a playwriting workshop. After experiencing enthusiasm from the attendees about the scene I wrote, I was inspired to begin developing a screenplay based on that scene. I am in the middle of writing that screenplay now, and this experience, like the singing, has brought me a rush of creativity and satisfaction. In addition, I began attracting more money. My relationships improved. My social life improved. I went from moving to a new city and feeling lonely to having an abundance of like-minded friends of various ages.

I believe these opportunities came to me because of an increased focus on my alignment, instigated by my desire to learn how to love and accept my body. It was fascinating to experience these "side benefits," especially for someone who has spent her entire life thinking you have to work hard to catch a break. The thing is, happy surprises can happen for all of us. Though the focus of this book is on learning how to love and accept your body and your food and release pounds (if releasing pounds is something you want), it is so much more than that. Your life will keep improving in ways you forgot you wanted when you put alignment first.

For example, if you want to transform your body into one that is more toned and fit, but you are, for the most part, in a state of unhappiness about your current body, you are keeping what you want (that new toned body) from manifesting.

When you begin to love and accept your current body *as is*, while making feeling emotionally good (alignment) your priority, you will eventually become inspired to take certain actions that will lead to the physical changes you desire. You won't have to force it. *It will become easy.* That is the experience of all the women I interviewed for this book.

There have been many times when I wasn't able to love myself and accept my body the way my Inner Being does. In fact, I've spent a lifetime *not* looking at myself the way my Inner Being does. (I no longer view that as lost or wasted time. Why? Because thinking about wasted time takes me out of alignment. As Maya Angelou said, "When you know better, you do better," and I know better now.) Sometimes I still choose to indulge in criticism about my body or my food, but I am more aware now. I know I am making a choice to either love and accept myself or to criticize and reject myself. As I said in Step 1, our Inner Beings would never agree with our feelings of unworthiness or that we weigh too much. Our Inner Beings love us no matter what. In fact, our Inner Beings celebrate where we are and everything about us *including* how much we weigh. At the same time, our Inner Beings want us to have everything we want, including the body we desire.

For some reason, we are truly convinced that if we criticize ourselves, the criticism will lead to change. If we are harsh, we believe we will end up being kind. If we shame ourselves, we believe we end up loving ourselves. It has never been true, not for a moment, that shame leads to love. Only love leads to love.

~Geneen Roth, author of *Women Food and God*

How to Break the Cycle of Criticizing Your Appearance

Have you ever caught yourself thinking negative thoughts about your body or your weight such as, "I can't believe how fat I am in that photo. Look at that double chin!" or "Look at the size of my thighs!" If you've engaged in these types of thoughts as much as I have, it is understandable to wonder how in the world you can possibly upgrade your self-talk. The solution to this dilemma consists of two words: soothe yourself. Try another thought such as, "I love and accept myself even though I look big in that photo." Or do your best not to look at the photos in the first place if they trigger you.

Your words have so much power. Every day, if you tell yourself, "I love you," if you give yourself one word of validation, it will change your mind.

~Ashley Graham, American model

What If You Can't Find a Better Feeling Thought?

Sometimes, no matter how hard you try, you simply cannot stop bullying yourself. You try to soothe yourself; you try to find relief in a new thought, but it seems impossible. You've built up too much momentum toward feeling the negative emotion (whether it's anger, disappointment, depression, guilt, shame, etc.). You've gone too far down the rabbit hole. I must admit, I've experienced times in my life when I've asked myself, "What would make me feel better right now? What can I think about or what can I do that would get me out of this funk?" And I could think of absolutely nothing. That's how low I was. It happens to the best of us. When you find yourself in this position, it's best to have a Plan B.

> I always wanted to be skinny and I struggled with getting there. Then one day I had an important exam at school I was preparing for and I didn't think about being skinny anymore. I wasn't worrying about it like I used to because I was too busy studying. Within a month I found myself losing inches and pounds without even trying. It was such a soothing epiphany to realize that I only have to do what pleases me and everything else falls into place.
>
> **—Paula**

Plan B: Try Changing the Subject

For me, Plan B usually consists of changing the subject. I think of something else that makes me feel good or, at the very least, makes me feel better. This takes practice, but before long, you'll get the hang of it, just as I did.

My husband, Steve, is a master at changing the subject. It took me about a year after we started dating to figure out what he was doing. Basically, if I bring up a topic he is uncomfortable with (he doesn't like talking about himself, for instance), he changes the subject and I immediately forget about what I just asked him.

One day I asked Steve, "You just changed the subject again because you don't want to talk about yourself, didn't you?" It became a joke between us as I watched him masterfully redirect conversations with me and others time and time again. He uses this technique to sidestep certain topics, which obviously makes him feel more comfortable. We too can use this approach to deliberately feel better.

Let's say you're in the middle of thinking negative thoughts about your body, your appearance or that delectable piece of tiramisu you just ate and the guilt you're harboring after succumbing to its temptations. You try to soothe yourself, but you realize very quickly it's not going to work this time. So you decide to think about something different—something that usually brings a smile to your face. You ask yourself, "What can I think about instead? What's something that always makes me feel good?" As you ponder, suddenly a picture of your two-year-old niece comes to mind. You see her cute cherub-like face with her big, beautiful eyes. You think about this Sunday when you'll see your sister and your niece Audrey, and suddenly you feel a little better. You think about the park you'll take her to and how much she loves it when you push her on the swing.

You decide to take a trip to the store on your lunch break to get your niece that special doll with the flowery shoes. You think about the smile on Audrey's face when she sees you and how she loves for you to brush her hair. Maybe you call your sister to discuss your plans and ask to speak to Audrey so you can hear her voice.

Distraction Is Your Friend

Suddenly you feel a little better, for you've distracted yourself from thoughts that were bringing you down. However, the negative thoughts try to pop back into your brain. They want to dominate your attention again, but you keep thinking about Sunday, your sister and Audrey and how good it's going to feel when she throws her arms around your neck and hugs you. Every time the negative thoughts creep back into your mind, you consciously choose to think about something else. You choose to think about Audrey, and you feel better.

Who or What Is Your "Audrey?"

What or who can you think about that would make you feel better whenever you need that distraction? It might not always be the same thing. The point is to find something that will lighten your mood—even just a bit.

Many people might say this is failing to face reality. Abraham's teachings do fly in the face of societal norms in certain ways. We're dealing in a different realm here. We're talking about energy and vibration. And if dwelling in a lower vibration keeps you perpetually at arm's length from what you want, why not raise your vibration by whatever means possible, as long as you're not hurting anyone?

Take Food and Weight Off the Table

One of my coaches named Tracy suggested I "take food and weight off the table." She suggested I stop thinking about releasing pounds and what I was or wasn't going to eat. She wanted me to take a vacation from the subject altogether and instead think about feeling good in my body. Every time I thought about my weight or food in terms of what I was eating, she suggested I change the subject.

Here's what happened...

I followed Tracy's advice and gave my thoughts a rest from thinking about my weight and worrying about food. As a result, I began enjoying my life and my food more. And I began to love my body too. The shame and guilt I used to feel about my body and my food began to dissipate. I also developed a deeper connection with my Inner Being.

Changing the subject in your mind is actually fun to do. With practice, it gets much easier. You will be amazed at how well this works! Abraham talks a lot about pivoting (turning your attention in a new direction), which is basically the same thing. The main objective is to feel better, so however you get there is up to you. Feeling better brings you closer to being solidly in alignment.

Shame is the intensely painful feeling or experience of believing that we are flawed and therefore unworthy of love, belonging and connection.

~Brene Brown, author of
The Gifts of Imperfection

The Shame Game - Lighten Up About Food and Weight

I've always been a strong advocate of coaching, even though I know we have access to all the wisdom we need right inside us. A good Law of Attraction/Abraham coach will encourage you to strengthen the relationship with your Inner Being and help you learn to trust your own guidance, which brings me to how I met my first Abraham Weight Loss coach.

In early 2017, I called my friend Karen in Florida (the one who led the Florida Abraham discussion groups I attended) and told her I was looking for a coach who had lost over 100 pounds and kept it off for over a year, and who had done it through the teachings of Abraham. Not that I needed to lose 100 pounds; I wanted to lose about half that.

However, I sought someone who could understand what it's like to feel overweight and obsessed with their body and food.

I called Karen because she knows a lot of "Abesters," as she calls them. Plus, if Karen didn't know anyone, I figured I would ask her to coach me even though she probably didn't weigh more than 110 pounds soaking wet, and probably never did except when she was pregnant—if then. Karen knows the teachings of Abraham better than anyone, in my opinion.

To my utter delight, Karen said, "I would be glad to help you, but do you know of a woman named Diana (yes, the same Diana who was in the Abraham-Hicks hot seat) who lost 100 pounds and is an Abraham-Hicks Weight Loss coach?" "What?!" I blurted. "She is exactly what I'm looking for! Boy, am I a powerful manifester!"

I immediately contacted Diana on Facebook, and she politely told me she did not have any openings for new coaching clients. I said, "No, no, no. You don't understand. I manifested you!" In any case, somehow, I convinced her to have one session with me. Long story short, she coached me for half-a-year.

The interesting thing is, during our twice-monthly phone calls, we rarely spoke about food. For the most part, we talked about guilt and shame—especially guilt regarding my personal relationships. These thoughts/emotions can weigh us down quite heavily. The shame and guilt we harbor is usually about other things in our life besides our food and bodies. Don't get me wrong. We did talk about the shame I felt about my body and eating habits, but these issues were surprisingly not the focus of every conversation. Diana helped me lighten up about the non-food or non-body related guilt I carried. These conversations provided immense relief and lessened my need to numb myself with food and TV.

But I Want to Release Pounds Now!

One of my coaching clients, Marianne, used to get frustrated because she wanted to release pounds now. She wanted to be thinner now. She wanted to stop having food mean so much to her now. *(Can you relate?)*

And then she would come back to Step 2, "Start a Love Affair with Your Body." It was when she finally began focusing on loving her body that she began to see results. You simply can't skip over this step. Not if you want long-term freedom from being obsessed with your body and

> Today I had a dessert when I wasn't hungry. The beauty of it is I didn't beat myself up over it. I aligned with the decision. I blessed the little lava cake with the sunken middle before I ate it. I said to myself, "The cells of my body know what to do with this cake. My body is amazing, and it knows how to digest this little piece of heaven. It is yummy and I am going to enjoy it and I am grateful for this unique dessert and all the care and love that went into making it."
> **—Linda**

your food. Not if you want a real transformation. Not if you want to love your body, your food *and* your life. It's a process, but you can do it. You do it by loving yourself. By being kind to yourself. By being patient with yourself. By accepting where you are now with your body while envisioning what you want to create.

One does not walk into the forest and accuse the trees of being off-center. Nor do they visit the shore and call the waves imperfect. So why do we look at ourselves this way?

~*Tao Te Ching*, classic Chinese text

Manifesting Love and Support

Surrounding yourself with loving, like-minded people is invaluable. It supports you on your self-love journey. I've had the opportunity to work with three Law of Attraction coaches, and they showed me how to think better-feeling thoughts as well as modeled soothing techniques for me. As a result, I started being nicer to myself. Over time, their voices replaced my critical voice, and eventually it was my voice that was doing the soothing.

Relationships are the playground of our existence. What better way to learn, grow and practice the Law of Attraction than inside our own intimate and not-so-intimate relationships. They make up the nitty-gritty of our experiences here on this planet.

If you don't have access to a Law of Attraction or Abraham friend or coach who can be that support for you, find a group online. Get the support you deserve. You are a powerful creator, capable of attracting the love and support you desire.

Today I asked my body what she needed,
Which is a big deal
Considering my journey of
Not really asking that much

I thought she might need more water
Or protein
Or greens
Or yoga
Or supplements
Or movement

But as I stood in the shower
Reflecting on her stretch marks,
Her roundness where I would like flatness,
Her softness where I would like firmness,
All those conditioned wishes
That form a bundle of
Never-quite-right-ness,
She whispered very gently:
Could you just love me like this?

~Hollie Holden, writer

Love Notes

Valerie The more you focus on what's wrong with your body, the more you get that experience.

Jessica I thought I would be happy when I was thin. I actually got happy when I started to love myself.

Charlotte I apologized to my body for not recognizing it as a gift.

Umi Everything changed when I started to love my physical self, cellulite and all.

Helen The more I wanted to lose weight, the more obsessed I became with losing weight.

Debbie Hating my body kept me hiding in the background, trying to disappear.

Marieanne Take your focus off the number on the scale and find a subject to feel really good about. Focus on that.

Linda I talked myself into loving my body. I'm kinder to myself now. I adore myself!

Sheila It always feels good to make peace with where you are. That's the first step.

Sandy I used to be so ashamed of my body. Now I love it. I move it a lot more and feed it foods it enjoys.

Chris Thank you, body, for carrying me through this life of mine. You rock!

Kristi I am such a magnificent, beautiful Goddess. I love how curvy and beautiful my body is. I love the shape of my hips and thighs.

Love Your Body Exercises

LOVE YOUR BODY EXERCISE #2.1

Change the Subject

Practice changing the subject in your mind whenever you find yourself having a negative or fearful thought about your body, weight, food or anything for that matter. Completely change the subject and think of something different that makes you feel better emotionally.

For example, on one occasion when I was criticizing myself for overeating, I realized I could think about my son who bought his first house in Colorado at the young age of 25. Feeling proud as a mom always brings a smile to my face. Thinking about a future trip to see him always makes me happy, too.

I started to change the subject whenever I caught myself worrying about something, and as a result, I began to learn how to get in alignment and stay there longer.

ANSWER THE FOLLOWING IN YOUR JOURNAL:

1. *What is a subject(s) you've been thinking about that has caused you to feel disappointed or anxious?*

2. *What are a few completely different subjects you can think about that would make you feel better right now (that might bring a smile to your face)?*

Sometimes if you're feeling very angry or upset, this exercise might not do the trick. Don't force it. If changing the subject isn't working, try a different technique to help you feel better.

As a child, I never heard one woman say to me, "I love my body." Not my mother, my elder sister, my best friend. No one woman has ever said, "I am so proud of my body." So I make sure to say it to my daughter because a positive physical outlook has to start at an early age.

~Kate Winslet, actor

LOVE YOUR BODY EXERCISE #2.2

In your journal, write an Appreciation List About Your Body

Write a list of 10 things you like or appreciate about your body.

It could include things you like about your body's appearance, functionality, longevity, flexibility or anything else you can identify.

Write only what feels good to you. If you feel a negative vibe when you write something, cross it out and write something else that feels good.

Here's an example of a list I wrote recently:

- I like my curly hair.
- I like how my cells know what to do.
- I like how my body keeps me healthy.

- I like my calves and my slender ankles.
- I like how my body responds to exercise.
- I like my waistline.
- I like my shoulders.
- I like my green eyes.
- I like how I look younger than my age.
- I like how my arms and back feel when I lift weights.

Here's an example of my friend Lorraine's list:

- I appreciate my body's inner wisdom.
- I appreciate my body carrying me through this life.
- I appreciate my beautiful teeth.
- I appreciate my wavy grey hair.
- I appreciate my muscular legs.
- I appreciate how my body tells me when it's hungry.
- I appreciate how my body loves a good massage.
- I appreciate how my body regulates my temperature.
- I like the shape of my nose.
- I appreciate how I'm able to hike the hills in my neighborhood.

I asked members in my Delicious Alignment Facebook group to tell their bodies what they appreciate about them, and here are some of their answers:

- You're full of light.
- Every inch of you is magnificent.
- You've supported and carried me around successfully and joyfully for so many decades.
- You are strong and have gotten me through every day of my life.
- You are so flexible, strong and graceful.
- You help me to feel, to taste, to see and to love.

- You allow me to enjoy frozen yogurt!
- You walk the dog, no matter what the weather.
- You allow me to do exercises that keep us fit.
- You gave life to six souls and nursed and carried them all so well.
- You're my soft place to fall.
- I live in you.
- I love all the hilarious noises you make.
- You are strong and healthy and beautiful.
- I couldn't live without you and you're quite adorable.
- You allow me to travel in this world. You are perfect and beautiful. I adore you.
- You are a magnificent piece of machinery who has healed and transcended things that I'm not even aware of. You move me to and through fantastic experiences. Body, I love you for all that and so much more. You are beautiful and powerful.
- You take me hiking into the woods!
- You allow me to have all these incredible experiences in the physical world. I can swim with you. I can run with you. I can touch with you. I can taste with you. I can feel the raindrops on my skin. I can put my feet in the river and feel the water underneath them. I can breathe in the fresh air with you. I can see a sunset with you. I can listen to beautiful classical music while holding my precious toddler in my arms with you.
- I love that my organs know what to do and do all kinds of stuff for me without my having to do anything!
- My body feels soft and silky to be in it. It's very, very responsive to me. It's my best friend.

The key is to find things you like and appreciate about your body. If you're having a rough time making the list, start with something as general as the intelligence of your cells, your body's ability to heal a wound or your fingernails' ability to grow.

Write a Longer List if It Feels Good

If more attributes keep flowing to you, keep going. Writing a longer list will add to the good-feeling vibes you'll get from doing this exercise.

Have fun!

This exercise will help you set the wheels of self- and body-love in motion.

LOVE YOUR BODY EXERCISE #2.3

Write a Love Letter to Each Part of Your Body That Could Use Some Lovin'

This exercise came from Paula (you will find Paula's story in Part Two). When I interviewed Paula, she described how she wrote love letters to each part of her body she didn't love—or that she felt needed some positive attention.

During the interview, Paula talked a lot about how when she was younger, her mother would often say, "Most of the women in our family have big thighs and a big butt. There's not much we can do about it."

At a certain point in high school, Paula noticed her thighs and derriere were getting bigger. She found herself terrified that her mother's belief about the women in her family would come true for her as well. She also had concerns about her knees due to a soccer injury at 16 years old. The doctors said she would never be able to ski, run or play soccer again.

When Paula discovered Abraham-Hicks in her early twenties, she decided to write love letters to those areas of her body that she either didn't like or was worried about. Amazing things happened after she wrote those love letters. She realized she could manifest the changes to her body she desired, including releasing pounds and inches around her thighs and butt, healing her knees and enjoying physical activities such as skiing and soccer again.

How to Write a Love Letter to Specific Parts of Your Body

There's no right or wrong way to do this exercise. Simply open your journal and start writing from your heart. That's it!

Here are a few tips that might help you get started:

Set a timer and write uninterrupted for three to five minutes without any editing or critiquing what you're writing. Just let the words flow like a stream of consciousness. You will often be amazed at what gets written this way. You may often reveal beliefs you never knew you held.

For instance, when I did this exercise and wrote uninterrupted, I discovered how much I really do love my thighs. I never knew that. I literally thought I still hated them. Turns out I don't! In addition, this exercise helped me develop a new level of appreciation for this part of my body. *(See the "Love Letter to My Thighs" on the next page.)*

Don't overthink it. The point is to "just do it," as Nike says, and whatever you wind up writing, try not to judge it. This is your love letter, and you get to do it your way.

Write a separate letter to each part of your body you think could use a little tender loving care.

Here's the Love Letter I wrote to my thighs:

Dear Thighs,

It seems I owe you an apology. Ever since I was about 15 when I started gaining weight for the first time, I've been criticizing you. I would think thoughts like, "You're too big." "You're not nice and small and thin like Susan and Connie's thighs." "You have cellulite and dimples and stretch marks." "You look ugly."

I felt ashamed of you and would hide you from everybody when I took you to the beach. When we went to Italy and everybody wore shorts, I wore long denim skirts. I didn't date for many of those younger years because I didn't want anyone to see you.

I really want to apologize for all those years of hiding you and criticizing you in my mind. The thing is, I realize now that I love you. I love you for all the places you've taken me throughout my life. I love you for hanging in there with me through all the ups and downs in my weight. You happily expanded and contracted with the rest of my body and continued to support me by physically taking me wherever I wanted to go.

I also want to thank you for responding so quickly to exercise when I go to Pilates class or walk up the hill or go hiking in the mountains. You really do like to build muscle and make me stronger. I like the way you're looking ever since we moved up here to Asheville. Also, when I think about it, you are an important part of my curvy figure I love so much.

The bottom line is, you've been with me through "thick and thin," pun absolutely intended. Today especially, I appreciate how much you've been receptive to my new image of my body. You really do respond nicely when I put my attention on how I want us to look. You're a great partner and friend.

I really love you and hope you can forgive me for all those years of making you wrong and wishing I had somebody else's leaner and longer thighs. You're my thighs and I want you to know I appreciate and love you. We're in this together and you are beautiful just as you are!

Love,
Me

Step 3
Create a New Story

When you start to believe that you will look a certain way, you are tapping into the power of beliefs to make it happen. Even if, in the beginning, you may be visualizing without belief, eventually the belief will come, as will all the power you need to achieve it.
~Jon Gabriel, author of *The Gabriel Method*

This step took me quite a while to learn because I seemed to get a charge out of telling and retelling certain stories that were actually counter-productive with regard to what I wanted.

It's crucial to know that if you want things to be different, you must begin telling a different story. You have to start telling it how you want it to be instead of how it is right now. This is also using **imagination and visualization.** Telling a new story is one of the key ways to learn how to love and accept your current body as well as transform it.

For the longest time, I held onto this particular story of why I was fat: my father was an alcoholic, and instead of turning to alcohol like my dad did to numb his feelings, I turned to food.

It's often difficult to give up a story you've grown attached to telling. But when you realize your story is a belief and that belief is nothing more than a thought you've repeated over time, you begin to understand you can create a new, empowering story that will liberate you from your past.

I had told that story about my dad for decades, but it was not serving me anymore. Every time I told it, I reinforced beliefs that I was a food addict. Addicted to sugar. Addicted to escapism through food and TV. Addicted to negative thoughts about myself. After learning about the Law of Attraction many years ago, I stopped telling that story.

When you want to stop telling a disempowering story, it's best if you replace that story with a new, empowering one. So that's what I did. My new story went something like this:

I am so happy I can celebrate and enjoy food and my body now. I love and accept my body as is, whether I've gained weight or lost it, whether I exercised or didn't, whether I ate what I consider healthy foods or unhealthy foods. I love my body and myself, but if I begin criticizing myself, I know self-love is a choice I can access again. I bounce back to feeling good about myself faster and faster, and I'm now at the point in my life where feeling good is my priority.

It's important your new story feels good when you think about it or tell it to someone else. If you create a story you find far-fetched, or that causes stress when you think about it, keep tweaking it until it brings you relief. The idea is to create a story that feels better than the old story—one that is believable to you now.

For instance, while the new story below is one I would love to manifest, it's not a story I can say without rolling my eyes and thinking sarcastically, *"Yeah, sure you can do that, Rhonda. Keep dreaming!"*

I am so happy I am now able to go on six-hour hikes with elevation gains of over 3,300 feet. I have the stamina and the strength to keep up with all the hikers in the group.

This story would be too far of a reach for me (at this moment in time). It would only frustrate me to try to tell such a story to myself or others. I would feel like a fraud. Creating a new story works only when you feel good when you tell it. Of course as we evolve, our stories also evolve, and what may seem impossible today may seem possible later.

Mass media tells people that having a double chin, stretch marks or dark areas on their skin is unsavory. But I'm here to change that narrative.

~Lizzo, performer

Susan Transformed Her Ice Cream Story

Susan, a teenage friend, used to tell the same ice cream story throughout the years. Susan described how, when she was about 10 years old, her mother would buy a pint of chocolate ice cream once or twice a week and eat the entire pint in one or two sittings, never offering any to Susan. As a pre-teen, Susan began to sneak little bites of her mother's ice cream from the freezer when her mom was out. One day, when her mother took the lid off her ice cream container and realized some of it was gone, she started screaming at her daughter. This became a regular routine, with Susan sneaking bites from her mother's ice cream and her mother getting mad at her. It wasn't long before Susan found herself secretly bingeing on ice cream as a teenager and into adulthood.

She became very unhappy with her body and weight, blaming it on her mom.

When Susan began studying Abraham and Law of Attraction, she realized that telling her ice cream story to others or even to herself was counter-productive to what she really wanted. She finally decided to stop telling the story because she realized it was one of the things keeping her fat. She eventually replaced that story with a new story, one that empowered her—a story about how she loved to exercise and eat healthy foods. It was a story about how she also enjoyed ice cream and no longer felt guilty when she ate it. Then she added another part to the story—before it actually happened: "I let go of weight eating ice cream."

Susan said it felt good to tell this story, so she kept it up. And to her absolute delight, she began to release pounds, even while occasionally eating ice cream. Susan soon replaced other disempowering stories pertaining to various areas of her experience with more empowering ones and found that process to be life-changing.

I had been dieting over and over again to change my self-image. Suddenly I asked myself, how about changing that around? Change your self-image first, and maybe the healthiest means to reach and maintain the new you will follow.

~Debbie Johnson, author of *Think Yourself Thin*

Tina Transformed Her Sibling Story

Tina kept telling the story of how, when she was growing up, she was known as the chubby daughter. Her siblings made fun of her, telling her she was fat and ugly and would never find a boyfriend. As a result of rehashing that story for decades, Tina kept reinforcing the experience of feeling fat and ugly.

One day Tina came upon Abraham-Hicks. After listening to Abraham audios for a few months, she decided to create a new story. She began telling the story of how she wanted to exercise more, how she loved fashion and loved helping women feel good about themselves, no matter what their size. Tina eventually lost more than 45 pounds and has kept it off for over 10 years now.

Telling an unpleasant, disempowering story is counter-productive because it lowers your vibration every time you tell it. So why bother? It's only keeping you from what you want to manifest.

> It's all about beliefs. I lost 50 pounds in six months by following a certain way of eating that I believed would work for me. I believed it would work and I believed I could do it and I believed the way I was eating was fantastically healthy. I also loved my food as I ate it and I loved my water and imagined it flowing through my body and making me healthy and strong. I believed if I stayed with the process, it would all work out, and that's exactly what happened.
> **—Jackie**

Where Do Your Stories Come From?

It's easy to understand how we developed our stories about everything from food to love. We grew up hearing things from those who took care of us, and we made judgments along the way—whether to adopt the beliefs of others or to believe something totally different.

Take food, for instance. You might have been raised in a household where your mother or father told you certain foods were bad for you and certain foods were good for you. Or you might have been taught that certain foods will make you fat and others will keep you thin. I constantly told my kids, "This is bad for you." "That is full of pesticides." "Sugar is poison." "Dairy creates mucus." "White bread is the devil." *(Okay, I'm just kidding about the white bread. Sort of.)* I'm still not a fan of pesticides, but knowing what I know now, I would have done things differently.

Don't get me wrong. I'm not saying we shouldn't teach kids about nutrition. I'm saying that instilling fears into children or adults about nutrition or lack of nutrition while leaving out the important piece about alignment is not the most beneficial way to go. I envision a world in the not-too-distant future where children are taught at a young age the importance of their beliefs and how they shape their lives.

There are countless beliefs and messages you can adopt about food and how it affects your body. Your current beliefs about food might have come from your parents, from school, TV, magazines or just about anywhere in your environment.

What I love about the Law of Attraction is you don't need to understand **why** you have a certain belief in order to change that story. You don't need to analyze your childhood or dig into your subconscious to figure out what happened and how it caused you to adopt a thought and repeat it over and over until it became a belief. (We'll talk more about the subconscious in a moment.) You don't need to figure out "the why." This isn't old-school therapy. This is about alignment and vibration.

You have to begin telling your story in a new way.
You have to tell it as you want it to be.

~Esther and Jerry Hicks, authors of
Money, and the Law of Attraction

Your Stories and Beliefs Determine Your Reality

After reading this far, you may have concluded that if what matters most is your vibration, it doesn't matter what you eat. You can eat anything you want and be healthy and at your ideal weight as long as you maintain a higher vibration (stay in alignment/maintain a feeling-good place for the most part). Actually, that is not the case. It **does** matter what you eat and here's why: No matter how good you get at maintaining a higher vibration, you still will always hold various beliefs about how certain foods, exercise regimens, personal metabolism, genetics, etc., affect your body. In other words, your beliefs, in addition to your alignment, play an important role in your health, fitness and size.

In addition, as you continue to seek guidance from your Inner Being regarding food choices, you're going to be inspired to take certain approaches unique to you. How do you wrap your mind around all these variables? You don't need to. All you need to do is eat in concert with your beliefs and follow through with those ideas that come from within.

51

Not one of the 25 women I interviewed who learned how to love their bodies using the Law of Attraction was guided to the same exact food plan or eating style. Each one of them ate according to her unique beliefs and was inspired to follow very different ways of eating. For example, one person followed the Ketogenic diet. Another person adopted intuitive eating. Yet another chose intermittent fasting.

I hold certain beliefs about what foods will make me gain weight and what foods will help me release pounds as well as what role exercise and drinking water play in the equation. These beliefs are different from your beliefs, which are different from someone else's beliefs. Here's the important take-away I really want you to hear: It's much easier to work **with** your beliefs than to work **against** them. Abraham calls this the "path of least resistance." (We'll talk more about the path of least resistance in Step 5.)

For instance, I hold a belief that any kind of restriction or any slight hint of the word "diet" imposed on my lifestyle will cause me to feel deprived and trigger a date-night with Netflix, a bag of barbecue potato chips and a pint of Cherry Garcia. I also believe if I eat those things, I will add two inches to my waistline, thighs and rear end overnight. And guess what? I will (because I believe it and expect it). On the other side of that same coin, I also hold a belief that my body responds quickly to exercise, so that's exactly what happens when I work out. I see results rather quickly.

Important to remember: When you follow the steps in this book, you'll discover what works for **you**. You'll learn how to act in harmony with your beliefs as well as choose good-feeling thoughts so you can trust your Inner Being's guidance every step of the way.

> *Your expectancy determines outcome, and as long as*
> *you're not attached to the outcome, the outcome will*
> *be guaranteed.*
>
> ~Deepak Chopra, author of *Quantum Healing*

Contradictory Beliefs

Here's an example of how your beliefs can affect your relationship with food: When you eat something you believe is bad for you or you believe is going to make you gain weight, you have a contradictory belief (Abraham calls it "split energy") about eating that food. You want to eat it, but you think it's a bad decision. There's a conflict going on inside you, usually called guilt, remorse or even self-loathing. You are conflicted not because the food is bad but because your beliefs about the food conflict with your desire to eat it. There is a self-fulfilling prophecy dynamic going on (because beliefs create realities). The (extremely) good news is your Inner Being understands not only what you want in your life and how to get you there—it also knows your beliefs and how to work with them to guide you to your desires.

What is the Solution to Contradictory Beliefs?

The solution is always the same: alignment—choose good-feeling thoughts and thus line up with the way your Inner Being sees life. Your Inner Being is always guiding you to your highest good, and when you're in alignment, you can actually perceive the guidance. If you're unable or unwilling to get into alignment at that time (I've been there), that's okay too. Do your best to think of a better-feeling thought about your body. Do your best to practice feeling good about whatever food choices you make. Do your best to feel thankful for what you're eating.

> I've never had any real worries about money. I always believed there would be enough and so there always was. And then it hit me. I have a powerful story about money, and a disempowering one about my body. I believed getting the body I want is hard, if not impossible. So, I asked myself, "What if attracting my desired body was effortless instead of difficult?" That would certainly change my experience, wouldn't it? Well guess what? It absolutely did!
> —**Amy**

Can You Change Your Beliefs?

Absolutely. By making alignment/feeling good your priority, you will change your beliefs over time because you will be practicing new habits of thought. At the end of this step are five techniques to access your imagination that can help you change your beliefs about food, your body or anything you want to attract into your life.

Here are some examples of self-limiting stories and beliefs:

I have a slow metabolism.
I inherited the fat gene from my grandmother.
I'll never lose weight.

On the flip side, I've heard women express empowering stories like these:

I love to exercise.
I'm in good shape.
I love my body and I let go of excess weight effortlessly and easily.

I bet you can identify many of your own contradictory beliefs, both empowering and disempowering. If you're unsure of your beliefs and stories, just take a look around you. Look at your world. Look at your finances. Look at your body. Look at your relationships.

Like it or not, your beliefs and stories have created your current reality. If you like what you see when you examine your life, great. Keep on thinking and believing what you've been thinking and believing. If there are aspects you'd like to change, you can begin by creating a new story or by using any of the other techniques mentioned in this book.

What About Subconscious Beliefs and Stories?

As a writer for online marketers for over 20 years, I worked with many business coaches whose specialty was clearing hidden beliefs that were secretly sabotaging their clients' successes. If you wanted to become financially successful, if you wanted to grow your business, you learned from these coaches how to uncover the subconscious beliefs blocking your prosperity.

If you've done any personal growth or business development work, you know addressing the limiting beliefs of your subconscious is a popular approach to curing self-sabotage. In the arena of weight, it's the same thing. Many weight-loss experts and coaches will guide you to explore subconscious beliefs holding you back from attracting your ideal weight.

You may have been taught to dig deeply and find the root cause of undesirable patterns of behavior in your own life. Many psychologists, life coaches and healers promote identifying the root cause of certain unwanted behaviors as a prerequisite for lasting behavioral change.

I know only too well about digging for the root causes of unwanted behaviors. I have a tall, rusty file cabinet in my garage filled with journals spanning over three decades. On so many pages from my teenage years through my 30s are entries describing how miserable I was at times because I went on yet another ice cream, candy or cookie binge. There are countless pages of me trying to understand why I did this. Why I self-destructed. Why, why, why, why, why? I spent endless hours writing about why I couldn't stop eating. I criticized myself time after time about my weaknesses, and I constantly focused on my unhappiness. I analyzed myself, trying to make sense of it all in hopes that I could find a solution. I wanted desperately to bring back that petite young woman who was now hiding inside a bigger, fluffier body.

I went to therapy. I went to a "fat farm" in Englewood, New Jersey, with my grandmother. I did lots of "inner work," trying to figure out the cause of my behavior. However, none of that soul searching seemed to make a difference.

Now I'm not a psychologist, and I don't aspire to be one. I understand that for some disorders, there may be a time for discovering root causes. However, Abraham teaches feeling better is what is most important (finding a better-feeling thought in the moment) when seeking changes in your behavior. You don't need to figure out "the cause," and you don't need to search your subconscious with either a shovel or a microscope. Abraham says whatever is active in your vibration will rise to the surface, so you will always know what to address by the way you are feeling. Your feelings are your guidance system. They let you know whether you're moving toward what you want or away from it. There's nothing to analyze. Nothing to figure out. All you need to do is find a way to feel better as soon as you can.

This method of making feeling better your number one priority works for me and it works for hundreds of thousands, if not millions, of other people on the planet—not only those who follow Abraham-Hicks but those who understand how the Law of Attraction works. (There are over 700,000 people who follow the official Abraham-Hicks Facebook page.) Abraham teaches if something needs to be addressed in your psyche, it will come up in the form of a thought that doesn't feel good. Simply said, that's when you deal with it. You deal with the thoughts and emotions that bubble up to the surface when you notice them. At that point, you do what works for you to think a better-feeling thought or to feel better in another way. Like attracts like. What you focus on comes to you. It doesn't get any simpler than that.

Don't worry about the subconscious mind. If it's subconscious, you're not feeling emotion. If you're not feeling emotion, it's not activated enough to matter a bit. The subconscious mind does not matter. It's the conscious thoughts that activate your vibration. People will say to us, I have just been in the worst mood for so long and I'm worried about my subconscious thoughts. And we say, that mood you're feeling isn't coming in response to your subconscious thoughts. It's coming in response to your conscious thoughts. Tend to your conscious thoughts.

~Abraham-Hicks, excerpted from Tarrytown, NY
5/10/03

For me, there is so much freedom and peace with this process. It's a freedom from the past. I've met many therapists over the years who study the works of Abraham and share how they've changed their techniques to focus very little on dredging up their clients' pasts. They focus on current thoughts and teach their clients how to soothe themselves: how to change their focus and feel emotionally better.

Imagine It the Way You Want It

When you read the individual stories in Part Two, you will be amazed at the huge role imagination and visualization played in each woman's journey to body-love and food-love. (Oftentimes we see food as the enemy. We'll talk about making friends with food in Step 4). Visualization works so well, is so easy to do, takes only a few minutes a day and doesn't cost a thing. How can we pass up this amazing tool? It's one of the fastest ways to transform the story you have about your body.

Your imagination is a wonderful, beautiful, amazing tool. It is the key to creating a new story about your body. We reveled in our imaginations as children, but as adults, we are expected to "face reality." Sure, if we were lucky, we were encouraged to dream big by the grown-ups in our lives. But rarely were we encouraged to use our imagination as adults in the same joyful way we did as children.

Meditate on the things you are doing as being already done—complete and perfect.

~Ernest Holmes, American New Thought author, teacher and leader

When you use your imagination on a regular basis to picture yourself having the life you want, including a healthy relationship with your body and food, you will begin to see changes in your behavior, your mood and your physicality. You will begin to shift the way you see yourself, and as a result, you will begin to manifest the vision of your body you hold in your mind. When you imagine your life and your body the way you want them to be, you are focusing on what you want. You are no longer focusing on the **lack** of what you want. You are imagining the toned muscles in your calves (for instance) and in your arms—whatever it is you would like to manifest, whatever it is you can line up with. Maybe you are not interested in changing your body. Maybe you simply want to learn to love yourself and your body as it is now. (It's about what **you** want. It's **your** body.) You are seeing what you desire with your mind's eye. You are imagining yourself comfortable in your own skin—proud of your body and living your life fully. You are seeing yourself in the new clothes, fitting into the dress or the new outfit (if that's what makes you happy). And as you are imagining it, you are reminding yourself to experience what it would feel like to love the body you're in and have the body you desire. You are feeling the feelings as if what you are visualizing is happening in the present moment. This is the key.

You can transform your beliefs and eventually your body and your life through your imagination.

Here are five techniques to help you transform your beliefs and stories by accessing your imagination:

1. Journaling
2. Vision Books or Boards
3. Emotional Visualization
4. Act As If
5. Speak It into Existence

1) Journaling

When I was working with my coach Tracy, she said, "I want you to journal. But don't journal about how things *are*, journal about how you want them to be. Journal about how you want to feel. You can take it a step further and write about how you are feeling as if what you want is *actually happening right now*."

So that's what I did. If I wanted to imagine myself fitting into my new jeans that were two sizes smaller than I was then, I wrote about how it felt to finally slip those jeans up my legs easily, without struggle. I wrote about how thrilled I was to realize I could pull up that zipper smoothly, as if it glided without any effort whatsoever, and I wrote about how it felt to fasten the button without having to suck in my stomach. I wrote about how it felt to move in the jeans and how easy it was to get in and out of the car while wearing them. I envisioned these jeans as the comfiest jeans I've ever worn!

Mindy, one of my coaching clients, shares an actual entry from her Visualization Journal about wearing a bathing suit without the skirt:

> *"I now wear a one-piece without wearing the skirt over it to cover my thighs. I know I didn't have to wear the skirt before, but I just didn't feel comfortable. Now I do. I visualized feeling comfortable enough with my body to wear the one-piece in public again. I visualized finally loving my body no matter what size it is. I remember wearing a one-piece and going swimming with my husband over 12 years ago. I remember feeling so sexy in that bathing suit, and now I feel that way again. Sure, I'm 12 years older, but I'm still sexy. I have a nice hourglass shape. I love my body even if it doesn't fit those images in magazines. I love the fact that it feels so good to wear a one-piece to the beach. And I love to move my body in the water."*

Mindy said her Visualization Journal played a big part in helping her feel comfortable wearing a one-piece again.

> *Write about how you want to feel in your body.*
> *That's a very powerful way to manifest the physical*
> *transformation you desire.*
>
> ~Tracy Branson, Fitness and Mindset Coach

2) Vision Books or Boards

Vision boards are also extremely powerful. A friend of mine, Angi, who attended a Business Mastermind group with me, created vision books (instead of a boards) every year. Angi explained, "Every time I achieve or receive something that's in one of my vision books (she needed more than one book because of all the things she wanted to manifest), I record the date and then add something new to attract." One year, Angi pasted a picture of a convertible car in her book. When I arrived for our Mastermind meeting in St. Augustine, Florida, she shared with the group that she just won a Mustang convertible in a Real Estate Agent raffle! Needless to say, she was thrilled. She was certain she won the car because of her vision book and proceeded to show us all the other previously manifested items in her book.

> *Dreams come true. The only variable is when. For the*
> *quick approach: Visualize. Pretend. Prepare. And*
> *give thanks in advance.*
>
> ~Mike Dooley, author of *Notes from the Universe*

I love how Mike Dooley talks about giving thanks in advance for whatever it is you are visualizing. You can add this to your process. Every time you add a photo to your vision board or book, you can say "thank you" as if it has already happened. This is a very important step because it demonstrates your belief in the Law of Attraction. It demonstrates your trust and faith in the process. If you can truly feel the appreciation for what you want to manifest as if it's happening now or has already happened, that means your expectation has lined up with what you want. And as Abraham says, "You get what you expect." You must believe it in order to allow it into your physical reality. That's pretty much how you manifest anything, including the body you desire.

> *The Universe does not know if you are offering your vibration because you are living what you are living, or because you are imagining that you are living it. In either case, it answers the vibration, and the manifestation must follow.*
>
> ~Esther and Jerry Hicks, authors of
> *Ask and It Is Given*

3) Act As If

Focusing on what you want is a major part of Abraham's teachings. If you want a new relationship, focus on seeing yourself in a new relationship. If you want a better job, see yourself happy in a new job. If you want to feel healthier, see yourself healthy. If you want to release pounds, focus on how you want to look.

In the past, money and weight have been the two sticking points for me. Instead of focusing on what I wanted, I focused on the lack of money or the lack of a smaller waistline. When I started to practice feeling like a prosperous person (acting as if), my bank account began to grow. Money came to me from unexpected places. When I started to practice feeling like a fit person, my body started to change into more of what I wanted.

Sometimes I view the manifestation process as a game, and I get so excited when something I've been focusing on manifests in my experience. I usually do a little happy dance.

If you want anything in life, including gaining or releasing pounds, adding more muscle to your body or simply learning how to love your current body, act as if it's already a done deal. Walk around with your head held high, as if the thing you want is already here.

"Fake it till you make it." "Keep your eye on the prize." "Mind over matter."

Some clichés lose their punch over the years, but others stick around forever because they are born from universal truths. As you build new habits of thought that focus on loving your body, you open the door for the manifestation, whatever it may be, to occur.

4) Speak It into Existence

Creating a new story for your own private contemplation is very powerful. But do you know what's even more powerful? Speaking it. Sure, there's that caveat about being careful who you tell. You want to share your new stories with people who will cheer you on as opposed to pooh-pooh your enthusiasm.

I'm very picky about who I share my dreams and goals with. That's why I surround myself with like-minded people. We hold the space for each other to speak about what we want as if it's already done. I'm less likely to share what I'm up to with people who don't understand the Law of Attraction because they might project their fears, concerns and "practicality" onto what I want to create.

But when I get in front of the right audience, watch out. Speaking what I want into existence is exhilarating. Having a group of supportive friends who "get you" and delight in your vision is invaluable.

The emotion behind your words is also important. The Universe hears the essence of what you're saying—what you're actually feeling. If you tell someone, "This deal is going to make me a millionaire," but you're secretly feeling, "I'm afraid this deal is going to bankrupt me," the Universe hears your true feeling. The key here is to say things that feel good to you.

5) Emotional Visualization

We've actually been talking about Emotional Visualization in each of the imagination techniques I mention here. Emotional Visualization is visualization on steroids and is the fastest way to bring a new story into existence. As I described above, you are creating a new story and you are imagining that it is either happening now or you are celebrating it having just happened. Your job is to feel the feelings of the celebration, the joy, the appreciation of having it come to fruition.

Laura shared how she visualized her body getting increasingly stronger while taking her daily walks. She imagined feeling her body building muscles and toning up every day. Audrey shared, "Seeing my slim body in my imagination was a major key to my success in releasing pounds. Visualization and allowing those good feelings to sink in were absolutely necessary in my process."

When I asked Jeana if visualization helped her go from a size 14 to a size 6 (she lost over 40 pounds), she replied, "Oh, absolutely. I have changed my world with visualization."

Love Notes

Danielle During my meditation this morning, my Inner Being gave me the inspiration to imagine my body as made of clay. It was so fun to reshape and sculpt it!

Steven I lost weight by visualizing how much I wanted to lose and what I wanted to look like. I felt the feelings as if I already had the body I wanted. Then the weight just fell off over a few months.

Millie I'm following my Inner Guidance and it's guiding me to wonderful places and experiences.

Que My life is so different now. I no longer base my worth on my size. This is such a huge breakthrough for me.

Kyla I write in my journal about what I want as if it's happening or already happened. Then I close my eyes and pretend it's happening right now. I have manifested lots of things I wanted this way.

Palak The key for me was to do anything and everything that buoyed me up in terms of my emotions, and then I didn't care about the weight.

Mary Jo Start having fun in your life. That's the secret to everything!

Margo I worked with my beliefs about food and weight instead of against them and lost over 70 pounds.

April Visualization changed my life. And it's so fun. I visualize things the way I want them to be.

Pegatha What do you want? See it in your mind. Feel it in your bones. Watch it become a reality.

Tami I gave up my old story and replaced it with a new one that included improved health. I visualized myself doing things that are easier with a fit and healthy body and it worked!

Love Your Body Exercises

LOVE YOUR BODY EXERCISE #3.1

Create a New Story

Identify a story you are telling (to yourself or others) about your body and/or relationship with food that is disempowering or creating something you don't want.

Next, create a new story about how you want things to be (make sure the new story feels good when you think about it).

EXAMPLE:

Current Story

I've always been overweight, and it's too late for me to change. I've tried to release pounds hundreds of times, and I've always failed. I guess I'm stuck at this size even though I don't like it.

New Story

I am feeling better and better about my body and my size, and anything is possible when I make feeling good my priority. I'm learning how to love and appreciate my body, no matter how much I weigh. I'm so excited about getting stronger and healthier. I'm also excited about loving and accepting my body while attracting improved health and fitness. I trust my body to tell me what it needs.

Write your old story and your new story in your journal.

It's not what you look at that matters,
it's what you see.

~Henry David Thoreau, author of *Walden*

LOVE YOUR BODY EXERCISE #3.2

PART A
Define Your Desired Body

If you would like to make changes to your body, it is very helpful to identify what you want.

Really think about what you want. If you're not sure yet, that's okay, but most of the women I interviewed had a clear picture of what size they wanted to be and how they wanted to look. Most were not concerned with a number on a scale. They wanted to fit into a certain size. For a few, weighing themselves was a useful tool, but most steered away from it. It's important to find what works for you.

Here's an example of a Desired Body Description:

> *I am fit and a size 10. I can comfortably fit into a medium or small size top. My arms are toned, not like a body builder, but triceps and biceps have some firmness. My tummy is almost flat as I like it with a little roundness. I have a curvy figure that I love. I fit into my nice bras from five years ago. My inner and outer thighs are toned. I look healthy and strong and feel good in my*

body. I am so happy and comfortable in my body and can move around freely and easily.

Write your description of your desired body in your journal.

Include not only how you want to look but how you want to feel in your body.

LOVE YOUR BODY EXERCISE #3.2

PART B
Visualize Your Desired Body

As we've discussed, visualization is extremely powerful. Your imagination is one of the most powerful superpowers you possess.

> *"I like to take about five minutes every morning after my meditation to visualize. I often will visualize by closing my eyes and imagining that I now have my desired body. I picture myself walking up the mountain by my house with no problem. I picture myself easily hiking with a group of people of all ages and enjoying myself. I imagine myself running my hands down my body and feeling the toned arms, the almost flat stomach, the curves of my body, the muscles in my thighs and the firmness of my back and backside. I pretend I am looking in the mirror, and I feel the emotions as if I have this body now and I am so happy. I feel so good in my body and love the way I look. I act as if the transformation has already happened, and I feel the feelings as if they have."*
>
> *– Ramona*

It is so important to "feel the feelings" during your visualization. This is the secret sauce that makes your visualizations work. Emotionless

visualization and emotional visualization are light years apart.
Visualization without emotion can work over time, but add the
emotion and watch your desires manifest more quickly into your life.
Emotional visualization will help you "become" what you want, and
when you "become" it, you can't help but manifest it.

**Practice visualizing how you want to feel in your body and write
about your visualization experience and insights in your journal.**

Step 4
Make Friends with Food

Food either evokes a feeling of guilt, or a feeling of resentment or a feeling of worry, when what it should bring forth is a feeling of appreciation, abundance, longevity, energy and well-being. Food is such an important component of your experience. We would befriend it and we would devour it with pleasure.
~Abraham-Hicks, excerpted from Monterey, CA
3/20/01

Many people spend a lifetime in a love/hate relationship with food. Can you relate? You crave a certain food and you can't stop thinking about it, and while you're obsessing about that particular food, you're thinking of all the reasons you shouldn't eat it:

It's bad for me.
It's going to make me gain weight.
I'm going to feel terrible after I eat it.
Why don't I have any willpower?

How Can I Stop Criticizing My Food Choices?

What I've learned from studying Abraham-Hicks' point of view on eating is our love/hate relationship with food is a recipe for everything we don't want. Being afraid of certain foods, focusing on what foods are bad for us and believing certain foods are going to cause us to gain weight creates the very things we are trying to avoid.

So instead of getting frustrated with yourself when you ate something you think you shouldn't have and asking, "Why did I eat this?" ask instead, "How can I align with what I just ate? How can I feel better about what I just ate? How can I raise my vibration?" Or even better, line up with what you're about to eat before you eat it.

Most of us who have felt "too big" in certain areas of our bodies have built up a lot of momentum in the area of judging everything we eat and feeling bad about ourselves afterwards.

A new practice can begin when we start changing the negative self-talk: easing out of that habit at every meal, every snack, every action or non-action. If we have a lot of practice in one direction (the direction of self-judgment, for instance), it may take a little time to build new habits of thought in another direction such as feeling good about our food choices, or at the very least, accepting them.

When you're outside the Vortex, anything and everything can cause an adverse reaction. And as you're scrambling around trying to figure out: "It might be this food or that food. I wonder if it's sugar or carbs. I bet it's the wheat. Yes, it's the gluten," and we say, it's not any of that. It's because you're not in the Vortex. You've got other outside-the-Vortex things going on that have your attention and that is keeping you from being in the Vortex. Period! Period! Period!

~Abraham-Hicks, *Happily Ever After* DVD 2011

You Mean It's Not About the Food?

That's right. It's not about the food. Abraham teaches your alignment is the deciding factor when it comes to how your body manages the food you ingest. Don't get me wrong. Abraham is not against eating healthy. They simply are not a proponent of beating yourself up when you're unhappy with your food choices. Criticizing yourself is detrimental because it lowers your vibration (takes you out of alignment), which ultimately gives you more of what you don't want.

Vibration Trumps Nutrition

Personal vibration and its effect on how your body processes food is a controversial concept for sure but one that makes sense in a world choreographed by the Law of Attraction. As I said above, your vibration overrides everything else, including nutrition. This in no way means that I'm advocating eating junk food as your main source of fuel for your body. However, it is important to understand that the way you feel about what you're eating has more to do with how your body will process the food than the actual food.

When you understand vibration and practice alignment, your love/hate relationship with food will gradually transform into a love/love relationship. The guilt begins to melt away. You begin to make friends with food, maybe for the first time since you were a child, before you began confusing food and weight with your self-worth.

Nutritional experts and others are sure to disagree with the statement, "It's not about the food." And that's okay. In a fully conventional perception of the world, this reaction is understandable. That's why I've written this book for people who follow Abraham-Hicks or people who understand the Law of Attraction. Mainstream, for the most part, may not be ready for this message. But you and I understand the role thoughts and emotions play in our physical reality, including our bodies. We are spiritual beings having a human experience. And because we are first and foremost spiritual beings, vibration trumps nutrition.

> Somewhere along the line, I learned that it is gluttonous to celebrate food. I have finally learned to enjoy my food unapologetically once again. Celebrating food has helped me become more aware of what I'm eating.
> I would say I'm more of a mindful eater now and that has helped me create a healthier lifestyle.
> **—Gloria**

Celebrating Food

I always thought there was something wrong with the fact I enjoyed food so much. Celebrating food in an unapologetic way, without shame, is something new for me. Maybe you've never had a problem celebrating food. If that's the case, you are one step ahead of the game. Like me, and many of the women who will read this book, celebrating food (without guilt) may not be something we've allowed ourselves to do. Learning how to replace food guilt and body shame with a joyous celebration of the food that nourishes, comforts and fuels us can seem like a radical concept.

Once I began studying food guilt and body shame, I realized that enjoyment of food is universal. I think I've met only two people in my entire life who didn't care much for food. Enjoying food is normal. Our hunger and craving for food help us survive. If we didn't enjoy food, if we didn't feel hunger, we might not eat, and that is probably not a good thing unless we've achieved the level of enlightenment of a self-professed breatharian who claims to exist on energy and sunshine alone. I, admittedly, am not one of them.

My friend Danielle, 53, who is also an Aber, is a wonderful example of how to celebrate and enjoy food fully. This baffled me at first. How could someone who frequently enjoys all kinds of food and beverages including cakes, chocolates and beer, who gets so excited and animated about food and loves to talk about it for days, maintain such a thin body?

I remember attending a house concert a few months ago for our violinist friend, Paul. The gathering was outdoors, and everyone brought a dish to share. While standing next to another skinny friend, Amanda, she reached for a cupcake and said, "Why am I eating this? I'm not even hungry. Oh well, it's no different than what I usually do."

I'm sure you know friends like this. It seems they break all the "eating rules" and still manage to be thin. Sure, everyone's metabolism is different, but what exactly determines your metabolism? (It may not be what you think. We discuss metabolism in Step 5.)

Today I have a better understanding of the answer to that question. Danielle and Amanda's energies aren't split about what they're eating. They don't have contradictory stories about their food and their bodies, which means they're not experiencing guilt and fear over their food choices. They have a pure energy stream when it comes to what they eat and how they look, and this energy stream is benefiting them and their bodies. (Energy stream means the thoughts we're sending forth into the Universe to be matched by the Law of Attraction.)

By learning to be okay with enjoying and celebrating food, by learning how to *make light of it*, by learning how to love and accept our bodies, we are encouraging freedom around the subject. We stop thinking of food as the all-too-seductive bad guy and our bodies as the unwilling victims. As a result, we experience more alignment.

Orgasmic Eating

Since I began this immersion into researching what Abraham says about food and weight, I started to attract different people from different circles into my life (not just Abraham circles) who spoke about "orgasmic" experiences regarding food.

Pegatha talks about her new experience with eating and how she now believes it was meant to feel orgasmic. "When you wait until you're really hungry to eat, you enjoy food so much more than when you are slightly hungry or not hungry at all," Pegatha says. "In fact, eating can be an amazing experience every time. It can be totally orgasmic. When you eat when you're hungry and stop when you're full, food will taste a hundred times better. It's like your taste buds explode when you eat. You find yourself saying things like, 'Oh my God, this is the best meal ever. I feel like I'm tasting this Vegetable Pad Thai for the *first* time in my entire life!'"

I'm not trying to give you another reason to feel guilty if you find yourself eating and snacking before you're super hungry. It's simply something to notice and have fun with—if you're so inclined.

Many other people I've spoken to have also realized they weren't enjoying their food to the fullest because their energy was usually split when eating (see "Contradictory Stories" in Step 3 for a description of "split energy"). There always seemed to be some sort of guilt or fear involved with food so they were distracted and not fully present to the experience. Therefore, their vibration was on the lower side, which interfered with their ability to have that exhilarating experience.

I still occasionally eat when I'm not hungry. And sometimes I still eat for sport. I'm not hungry, but I want to enjoy a treat in front of the TV. It's often the way I relax. When this happens, I now say to myself, "It's okay. I want this and I'm going to enjoy it even though I'm not hungry and even though it's after 7pm and even though it's full of sugar. My body knows what to do with it. It's not about the food anyway. It's about how I'm feeling while I'm eating the food." So I line up with it as best I can and eat it. I don't make a big deal over it anymore. And guess what? Now that I've made this type of eating no big deal, I do far less of it.

Eating in a way that makes you feel out of control is either from restriction, or a resistance to being in your body and feeling, and often both at the same time.

~Caroline Dooner, author of *The F*ck It Diet*

Deprivation Is Exactly What It Sounds Like

On the opposite side of celebrating food and orgasmic eating is deprivation. If you're reading this book, then there's a good chance you have some experience with deprivation when it comes to food because there's a good chance you have experience with the other "D" word: dieting. Just the very mention of the word makes many women cringe, me included. Deprivation and dieting don't work very well long term.

We've heard it a million times. And yet the weight loss and diet control market in the United States is a $72 billion industry, up from $68.2 billion in 2017. Despite this increase, the good news is "the number of dieters has fallen, due to the size acceptance and body positivity movement," according to researchandmarketing.com. The more we continue sharing the message of body love and acceptance, the more the number of dieters will continue to fall—over time.

The more we learn how to love and accept our current bodies and connect with our true selves (our Inner Being), the more we create what most people on this earth crave: a sense of well-being and spiritual awe.

But I digress. Let's get back to the still-pervasive dieting culture which, by its very nature, is fueled by the act of deprivation.

Here is Merriam-Webster's definition of the word deprivation:

"1.   the state of being kept from possessing, enjoying, or using something: the state of being deprived"

"2.   an act or instance of withholding or taking something away from someone or something: an act or instance of depriving: LOSS"

Dictionary.com's definition of the word deprive is: "to remove or withhold something from the enjoyment or possession of (a person or persons)."

"Understandably, every diet has taught you not to trust your body or the food you put in it."

~Evelyn Tribole and Elyse Resch, authors of
Intuitive Eating

I no longer criticize myself for eating certain things or for not being slender. I focus on what makes me happy, and as a result, I feel more comfortable in my skin. I'm losing weight but that isn't as important as it used to be. Living a healthy lifestyle and enjoying my life is what's important now. It's a great way to live!
—**Robin**

What is the Vibration of Deprivation?

The vibration of deprivation hovers in the same vicinity as punishment and hardship. The diet industry teaches us to deprive ourselves. And it stands to reason if someone needs to be deprived or punished, then that means they must have done something wrong. That's where the shame and guilt come in. These are very low vibrations when you're trying to transform your body or simply learning to love it. No wonder diets don't work! You're working against yourself when you're depriving, punishing or shaming yourself. Deprivation is the opposite of what most people want to experience. When you deprive yourself, you are literally removing or withholding something from your enjoyment. There's not much freedom in that.

What About Willpower and Moderation?

This is a good question. From a Law of Attraction perspective, forcing anything (willpower) is the hard way of going about it. Inspired action…that's a whole different ball game. Inspired action is easy. It flows. It feels good. Not one of the women I interviewed for this book said she learned to love and transform her body through deprivation or even willpower. Instead, they shared how they deepened their relationship with their Inner Being and followed the guidance they received when it came to food and everything else in their lives.

Sure, some women were guided to join various weight-loss programs and some were inspired to try specific food plans such as Keto or plant-based eating. Many released pounds while on these programs and plans and are continuing to do so. The point is they were inspired to take those actions. They did not force them.

Most of the women I interviewed were guided to what you might call intuitive eating. They learned how to listen to their bodies. They asked their bodies, "What do you want right now?" And they began to get better and better at trusting the answers they received—even if their body answered, "I want a donut."

Again, I'm not promoting an "eat-anything-you-want-including-huge-quantities-of-candy-for-dinner-every-day lifestyle." We'll talk about choosing an eating style that's right for you in Step 5. However, the women I interviewed reported a freedom around food and their bodies when they put alignment first. They weren't so wrapped up in the constant judging of their last meal and the impatient longing for the next. They learned how to inhabit a body that requires food for sustenance minus the obsessiveness, shame and guilt—but never without the pleasure. They learned to listen to their intuition, eventually finding a way of loving and transforming their bodies that worked for them.

> When I first started quieting my mind and getting in touch with my Inner Being, I was still eating the way I used to eat. I didn't change my diet all at once. Gradually, however, I started noticing I was becoming more interested in what is traditionally thought of as healthier foods. It wasn't something I tried to force on myself. It just happened naturally, the more I grew spiritually.
>
> **—Tami**

You May Become Attracted to Higher Vibration Foods

We choose foods based on where our vibration is at the time, even if we are unaware that we're doing so. The closer a food is to its natural state, the higher the vibration it holds. When we are in a high vibrationally-allowing state, we are often prompted to choose more natural and less processed foods because their vibration matches our vibration.

In other words, the more in alignment you are, the more you may eventually be attracted to higher vibrational foods. The key word here is "eventually." So don't be hard on yourself if you're not instantly eating kale and beet salads all day long. It's okay if you are attracted to a variety of foods you consider "healthy" and "not healthy." I know plenty of thin people who seem to be vibrating at a high frequency whose idea of a vegetable is an onion ring. Your Inner Being will take you on a journey that will lead you to the easiest path for you in this moment. (Again, we'll talk more about the path of least resistance in Step 5). Sometimes that path might look like a double cheeseburger with fries and a salted caramel milkshake (yes, I'm getting hungry) or other foods you would not equate with a higher vibration or a "healthy choice." The question is, do you want to keep dieting and berating yourself for not sticking to the "healthy" regimen you would follow if you were "being good," or do you want to deepen your relationship with your Inner Being and trust where it leads you? Remember, Source has all the data when it comes to you and your desires and is orchestrating things in your favor. If you begin eating what you consider "healthier" foods—great. In the meantime, if you make your alignment your number one priority, your entire life will begin to improve, including the way you feel about your body, your health and your food.

Granted, sometimes things won't make sense because why in the world would your Inner Being want you to eat a bowl full of nachos smothered in queso and sour cream if your desire is to manifest a more-toned body? As I said before, and I'll say again because it is that darn important: trying to use willpower to deprive yourself of a particular food you're craving creates more resistance (negative thoughts and feelings). Case in point: Try "not" thinking about a pink elephant. All you can think about is the pink elephant, right? Now turn that pink elephant into something you're craving like a piece of chocolate cake and all you can think about is...the chocolate cake, despite all your efforts not to.

Learning how to trust your Inner Being and your body eventually leads you to the body you desire as opposed to going about it through willpower and deprivation.

When you feel fat, your food makes you fatter—it does! When you feel slender, your food keeps you slender—it does! You must understand that, because you see people eating similarly with very different results, and you say, "Oh yeah, it's their metabolism," and we say, "What do you think metabolism is?" Metabolism is a vibrational response to your moment in time. Metabolism is the way the energy is moving through your body. And so "everything" is in response to the way you feel. Everything is. Everything is mind over matter.

~Abraham-Hicks, Alaskan Cruise, July 2016

Your Thoughts Determine Your Metabolism

The above quote is yet another Abrahamism that takes the phrase, "It's not about the food," to a whole new level. This quote brought so much clarity to me that I want to go through it line by line. Such a bold statement deserves a closer look.

"When you feel fat, your food makes you fatter—it does! When you feel slender, your food keeps you slender—it does!"

Okay, so we've talked about how our thoughts affect how our body processes food. Now we get an even clearer picture—another clue that cannot help but cause us to ask ourselves, "Am I feeling fat, or am I feeling slender?"

(We'll use the word "slender" here since that is the word in the quote above. You can replace the word slender with any words you like, such as fit, sexy, beautiful, handsome, in love with my body, etc. I'm not suggesting that slender is the right or best way to feel.)

Back to the quote. As startling as it seems, the same burger and fries will have a different effect on your body depending on whether you feel fat or slender. And the same kale and beet salad will have a different effect on your body depending on whether you feel fat or slender.

So you might as well eat the burger and fries, right? That is up to you. There is nothing wrong with eating the burger and fries. However, if you believe the burger and fries will make you gain weight, then guess what? Your beliefs make it so. The bottom line is to focus on feeling the way you would like to feel as if you've already obtained the thing you want (emotional visualization as described in Step 3). If you want to be slender, then focus on feeling slender. If you want more health, then focus on feeling healthy. If you want to love and accept your body as is, then focus on loving and accepting your body. (It's not about the burger and fries. It's about how you feel about eating them.)

"You must understand that, because you see people eating similarly with very different results, and you say, 'Oh yeah, it's their metabolism,' and we say, 'What do you think metabolism is?' Metabolism is a vibrational response to your moment in time."

My favorite part of this quote is, "Metabolism is a vibrational response to your moment in time."

Every moment is a new moment. Every moment is a new opportunity. What if your last moment was a low vibration? So what?

This is a new moment. And here's another one. And another. How can you feel better right now? In other words (and I hope this makes you as excited as it does me), each improved thought and feeling equals an improved metabolism.

Let's say you just ate an entire box of Valentine's Day chocolates. What size box, you ask? One of those big heart-shaped boxes—the $24.99 kind. So what? Choose a better feeling thought now. Raise your vibration now. As soon as you can, get in alignment with the fact that you ate that chocolate. Criticizing yourself about it is only going to make you lower your vibration and your metabolism. Soothe yourself about the chocolate. "Okay, so I ate the chocolate. I still love myself. And the chocolate was so good. I wanted it and I had it. Anyway, it's not about the food. It's about what I think about the food. Everything is still working out for me, and all is well."

Look, I know it may be hard for some of us to quickly forgive ourselves for eating an entire box of $24.99 Valentine's Day chocolates. And I realize how irrational it sounds to say that you won't gain weight eating like this. The point is to get increasingly better at making light of the situation. To get increasingly better at soothing yourself. To get increasingly better at feeling good. When you really get that it's not about the food, you begin to see the value in being kinder to yourself.

"Metabolism is the way the energy is moving through your body. And so 'everything' is in response to the way you feel. Everything is. Everything is mind over matter."

There's not much room for interpretation here. Everything is in response to the way you feel.

Sometimes I feel so aligned. So inspired. So amazed by the miracles of life. And other times, I find myself feeling frustrated. Down. Or even depressed. And I don't know why. "Why am I sad or frustrated?" As I spoke about in Step 3, you don't have to figure out "the why" anymore. It's not important. You can go directly to, "How can I feel better? What would make me feel better right now? Should I take a walk? Should I watch a comedy? Maybe what I really want is to cuddle up with my husband. What thought will make me feel better?" This is so important because, as you can see, our thoughts and feelings affect our metabolism.

"Everything is mind over matter."

We've heard this saying many times. When a phrase is overused, it eventually loses its impact. (The phrase, "mind over matter," has been around since it was coined by Sir Charles Lyell in 1863.) But when you take it literally, which I think is the only way you can take it, it is quite a powerful statement. Our bodies are matter. And according to this quote, everything is mind over matter. Therefore, it is safe to conclude that our mind controls our metabolism.

Could it be this simple? Could it be that all we have to do is "feel slender" or "feel fit" or "feel in love with our bodies" to eventually manifest the body we desire or love and accept the one we have? I can tell you this: the women I interviewed would all say a resounding yes, it is this simple. Feel the feelings as if you are already there.

This is the work.

What About Food Cravings?

What do you do when you experience cravings for foods you think are bad for you? The majority of women I interviewed said if they had a craving for a certain food they thought was "unhealthy," and they chose to eat that food, they learned how to trust their bodies and their Inner Being and stop feeling guilty over it. In other words, they ate it and enjoyed it! They practiced loving themselves anyway. They practiced getting in alignment (feeling okay) with the decision to eat that certain food or drink that certain beverage. Still, what to do about food cravings is one of the most frequent questions I receive on social media. So let's plunge deeper into the subject.

Why We Have Food Cravings

We have certain cravings for foods or substances we might label as "bad" because our bodies are accustomed to having that specific food or substance. Whether it's sugar, alcohol, a drug or a bioidentical hormone, our bodies adjust to having that ingredient in our system. Another

> If it's a healthy meal, I tell myself, "This is so good for my body. The weight just drops off me when I nourish my body in this way." If the meal/snack is what I consider unhealthy, but I'm having a craving for it, I tell myself, "This food is feeding my soul. My body needs a treat and my cells know exactly what to do with it. This food is fueling my spirit and I will savor every bite." My metabolism has traditionally been slow, but since I've been telling this new story, my whole experience has changed.
> **—Melissa**

possible reason we might crave a certain food or substance we think is detrimental to our health is because we feel disconnected from our Inner Being, and we are trying to fill that void with something we find enjoyable. We want to feel better now. While nothing can fill the void except alignment, that doesn't stop us from attempting to fill the void in other ways.

Your Body Adjusts to Whatever You Give It

Your body knows how to keep itself balanced. Abraham says when you ingest something that your body is not used to, such as a chemical added to processed foods, it knows how to make the necessary adjustments and recalibrate itself back into a healthy state. Your body, being the brilliant collection of trillions of intelligent cells that it is, adjusts to the introduction of whatever you have given it.

Science shows certain foods have more nutritional value or human fat producing traits than others. However, Abraham's teachings tell us our beliefs and our vibration supersede everything else, including the current scientific understanding of food.

This is not to discourage you from eating foods that are considered healthy but rather to encourage you to align your energy with the choices you make.

Love Notes

Annie Today, if I have a desire to eat something and I choose to eat it, I align with that decision.

Carla I'm learning how to live in ease and flow when it comes to my body and my food.

Sudika I love to eat out with my friends. I love how people put love into preparing dishes for me.

Emily What a wonderful realization that our weight has nothing to do with what we eat.

Sophia I don't want to stress about food and weight anymore.

Amelia You can eat whatever you want as long as you feel good when eating it because it's not about the food – it's about your alignment.

Cat Dieting and deprivation are setups for binges. Just sayin'.

Rachel I love food.

Cynthia Your Inner Being will tell you what it wants to eat. All you have to do is listen.

Denise Food tastes AMAZING when I'm really, really hungry. But sometimes I eat after I'm full and I don't even taste the food. I don't make a big deal out of it anymore and as a result, it seems to be happening less and less.

Brooke Food is my friend and I love my friends.

Sonali I am so happy with my fit body. I love vegetables, fruits and chocolate. I love that I can eat whatever I want without gaining weight. I love to clean up my vibration regarding all foods.

Love Your Body Exercises

LOVE YOUR BODY EXERCISE #4.1

Align with Your Food Choices

Mentally survey the past week. Write down in your journal any times you found yourself criticizing any of your food choices.

Example: On Wednesday, I ate bread pudding with whipped cream late at night, and I was upset with myself afterwards and the entire next day.

What can you think or do differently next time you find yourself criticizing your food choices? (Write your answer in your journal.)

Example: I could tell myself one or more of the following:

- *"It's okay that I ate the bread pudding because it's not about the food. It's about how I feel and think about what I ate that really matters."*

- *"So what if I had a late-night dessert? I rarely do that anymore, and it's not a big deal. What matters most is my alignment."*

- *"Today I'm going to focus on forgiving myself for eating the bread pudding. Maybe I'll do something fun with my friend to help me get in a higher vibration."*

The more empowered you are with your thoughts, the more empowered your metabolism is.

~Judy Legare, Certified Eating Psychology Coach,
Institute for the Psychology of Eating

LOVE YOUR BODY EXERCISE #4.2

Ask Your Body What It Wants

When you get hungry today, ask your body, "What would you like to eat? What do you feel like having? What would make you feel satisfied?"

Practice listening to your body and trusting the messages you receive without judging or criticizing the answers from your body and Inner Being.

Write a few sentences in your journal about your insights after doing this exercise.

Step 5

Build Momentum Toward the Body You Want

Once you make a decision, the universe
conspires to make it happen.
~Ralph Waldo Emerson, philosopher and writer

I learned how to love my body while writing this book (and I'm still learning). However, I hit many walls along the way. Big, giant brick walls that made me want to give up this book project all together. That's why it took me so long to write it. I kept pushing it aside, unable to deal with the subject matter that would ultimately make me vulnerable to the judgment of others. As I mentioned in the Introduction, I was afraid. Afraid of making a fool of myself. Afraid of being criticized. Afraid people would think, "Who is she to write this book? She's not thin." "These steps didn't work for her." "She's a fraud."

It's true. Though I've gone down three sizes and am a size 14 at this writing, that may not be society's version of "thin." And that's okay because I realized this book is not a "How to Get Thin" book after all. Maybe that's how it started out, but as I explained earlier, it has morphed into a "How to Love Your Body and Your Self" book. For the first time in my life, I'm not basing my worth on the size of my thighs.

The point of this book is to learn how to love and accept your body now and stop putting pressure on yourself to reach a certain body type—a body type someone else defined for you. (Perhaps that "someone else" is the fashion industry who, once upon a time, chose the skinniest of fashion models to model their clothes because the curvy women upstaged their frocks?) If you're like me, you unknowingly bought into the skinny body type as the gold standard you must reach in order to be a worthwhile citizen/female of your community, country and world. All hail the Queen of Thinness—because if you're not thin, you don't count. Well, we've had enough of that, wouldn't you say? Life is too short (unless you believe in reincarnation) to do anything other than love yourself as you are while manifesting who you want to be.

The Sweet Taste of Momentum

I talk a lot about momentum in this book. Once you begin building momentum toward loving and accepting your current body while, at the same time, focusing on transforming your body (if that's what you want), there's no stopping you. Things begin to click. Insight comes to you. You begin seeing results.

Full disclaimer here. The following is not a personal commentary on how being fat is bad. This is my personal experience. What I desired is to have a somewhat smaller body because 1) I like the way I look a few sizes smaller and 2) It's for my health and longevity. My body feels healthier at a size 12/14 than at a size 18. (My joints hurt less, my plantar fasciitis and digestive issues goe away, my sleep apnea lessens, etc.). I also feel healthier when I work out. That's my belief and my preference, and as I explained in Step 3, it's much easier to work *within* your beliefs than to push against them. (Whether people are actually healthier at a smaller size is irrelevant here because what we're talking about is working within your beliefs. These are the beliefs *I have* about my body.)

As an aside, while I was writing the above "disclaimer," I kept feeling that I was making justifications for wanting to be smaller, as if the body positivity movement is bashing those of us who want to release pounds. It's not. Or at least, I hope it's not. Because it really should be about choices. Loving yourself no matter what size you are *and* loving yourself if you want to make changes as well.

Okay, now that we have all of that out of the way, let me tell you about the big aha! moment I experienced that caused ***my*** momentum to kick in. After many months of wondering why releasing more pounds wasn't easier for me (after all, the women I interviewed said releasing pounds was easy when they implemented what they learned from Abraham and other similar mindset philosophies), I became frustrated. Then it hit me. "You have gone back to walking around feeling like a fat person who is ashamed of being fat. Despite everything you are preaching in this book, you are stuck in the 'what is-ness' of your body. True, insight after insight is bursting like chocolate caramel popcorn in your brain, and true, you are living and breathing this Law of Attraction secret sauce and having breakthroughs in so many areas of your life, including your relationships, career and money, but you are still feeling fat and feeling shame about feeling fat."

And then I remembered the quote from Step 4, "When you feel fat, your food makes you fatter—it does! When you feel slender, your food keeps you slender—it does!"

"No wonder I'm still fat and ashamed!" I thought. "I keep feeling fat and ashamed. As a result, no matter what I eat, I'm going to be fat. No matter how much I exercise, I'm going to be fat. As long as I keep feeling fat and criticizing myself for being fat, I'm going to keep being a fat woman ashamed of her fatness."

That was it! That was the missing piece for me. I had temporarily forgotten to incorporate the concept of "acting as if" into my life. I had fallen back into the habit of feeling fat and feeling embarrassed about it. I was still basing my worthiness on my weight.

I went back to Step 3: Create a New Story. I knew I had a belief that I was unattractive whenever I felt fat (story, not truth). So what did I do? I decided to use my imagination to help change my beliefs and my story. I imagined that I was already living in a smaller, fit body. In other words, I started *acting as if*. (I talked about Act As If in Step 3.) I started acting, thinking, moving and "being" like a person with physical confidence. I began *believing* I was a fit, sexy, attractive person.

I decided to replace every "fat" thought with an "I love you" thought. In addition, when I put my underwear on in the morning, instead of looking at it and thinking, "Oh my God, these bloomers look ginormous!" (my grandmother used to call them bloomers), I said, "I am beautiful just the way I am. I've built up momentum toward loving my body. There's no stopping me. I am sexy. I am worthy."

Now if those words made me feel bad, I would use different words. The point is to find the words and thoughts that bring you relief. If saying "I am beautiful," makes you feel bad in that moment (because you can't line up with that thought), then don't say or think that thought. Think or say something that is an improvement from your current thought.

Continuing with the theme of acting as if, when I ate a gluten free chocolate chip cookie, or two, or three or four and said, "Why did you eat all those cookies? Now you've raised your blood sugar level and that makes you gain weight," (another story), or "Why did you have to eat them at night, after 7pm?", I replaced those thoughts with new ones. It went something like this: "It's not about the food. It's only about the food when I believe it's about the food. It simply doesn't matter. Those cookies have no power over me. I am healthy, fit, sexy and everything is always working out for me."

And when I didn't exercise for a week or more for whatever reason and began thinking, "Oh, look at these arms. I could fly to California with these wings." "Look at my thighs. There's enough fat there to give someone a Kim Kardashian butt." "Look at this stomach. I look pregnant," I replaced those thoughts with, "It's not about the exercise. It's about my thoughts and beliefs *about* the exercise. It's okay that I didn't exercise in three days. I was busy. I'll get back to exercising tomorrow. Besides, I am healthy and beautiful and everything is always working out for me. I attract wonderful friends and fascinating experiences into my life. I love myself."

Some people might consider it conceited to replace negative thoughts with such seemingly boastful thoughts as those above. But is it really? Confidence is something I had to teach myself. I love my parents very much, but confidence was frowned upon in my family. Confidence in my house was met with silence accompanied by "the look." I realize this is a story I have about my family, and my new story is this: It's okay to be confident. Not only is it okay, but when you're confident, you make it okay for others to feel confident. Rev. Dr. Barbara R. Waterhouse, Co-Founding Minister of Center for Spiritual Living Asheville, where my husband and I attend, models confidence for thousands of us at the Center and online *(cslasheville.org)*. She often says she wakes up in the morning, looks in the mirror and says, "You look gorgeous today. You are amazing. You are a good lookin' woman!" She is 65 years old and is indeed beautiful inside and out. Barbara also shares how people often are uncomfortable with her confidence. They'll say she is conceited or full of herself, but she doesn't care. She knows what she's doing. She's modeling self-love for the rest of us.

Inspired Eating

Confidence is more than feeling good about your appearance. It has to do with trusting your Inner Being to guide you in all areas of life, including what to eat. In fact, that is the definition of inspired eating. Whether you're guided to eat vegan lasagna or a fully-loaded pizza, inspired eating is when you make your decisions based on what your body is telling you it wants. And whatever you decide to eat, you line up

> I've been practicing aligning my thoughts and raising my vibration to correlate positively with food for about a month. This is a major challenge for a girl who has struggled with an eating disorder where I'd be terrified of eating anything at all. I've been listening to my body and eating literally whatever I want to, and I haven't gained any weight! I've relaxed about food and focus on my vibration which to me means being happy and loving myself. This Delicious Alignment group has helped me stay focused and inspired. It really does work. I'm amazed.
> **—Steafene**

with your decision as best you can. In other words, you practice all the tools we talk about in this book to feel good about what you eat—before, during and after eating it.

If you eventually are guided to eat more nutritionally dense foods (which may happen when you follow these steps), that's great. However, the initial goal is to learn how to trust your body and your guidance, discover how to love and accept your current body, shed the shame and guilt typically associated with food and body image issues, and realize you have the capacity within you to create the body you truly desire.

When you practice inspired eating, you build new habits of feeling relaxed about food. You are at peace about it because you know your true state is well-being. You begin to make friends with food, and you are looking for inspiration and guidance in all things, including when to eat and what to eat. Your body tells you when it's hungry. If what your body wants to eat is not available, you trust that your body will still be able to absorb what it needs from whatever you choose. If this sounds like a fantasy, don't worry. New habits usually happen gradually. But make no mistake, this way of being and eating is available to you when you begin to make choosing thoughts that feel good (alignment) your priority.

Learning how to trust your body doesn't mean you'll never be out of alignment while eating again. It's about practice, not perfection. And as we've discovered, there are no right or wrong foods to eat. Still, you may experience ups and downs in your mood, especially if you have a long history of trying to control your weight with dieting. Feeling like you've taken a few steps backwards is not the end of the world because now you know what to do when this happens. You have techniques to choose from to help you re-connect with your Inner Being. When you stop looking at setbacks as failures, and instead look at them as opportunities to learn more about what you really want, you spend less time in disappointment and more time in positive expectation. This is the basis for manifested desires.

Challenges Offer Clarity

We do not come to this earth to experience a conflict-free life. Yes, Abraham says we come here for joy, but Abe also says experiencing contrast (variety of life that includes challenges) is part of the deal we signed up for. When we agreed to come to this physical world, we knew joy was the purpose, and contrast would help us get there by assisting us in clarifying what we want.

Everything you've been through regarding your body and weight and your relationship with food—everything you have viewed as a struggle or wasted time—has **not** been a waste of time. Contrast is not the enemy. There is no backwards. There's only alignment or non-alignment. The contrast serves a purpose. It helps us identify what we want. Without it there would be no expansion. (I'm talking about the spiritual kind of expansion).

So when you realize you're out of alignment (out of sorts, in a negative frame of mind), determine to get back in alignment as soon as you can. Everything falls into place when you do this one thing.

> *When you get tuned into this high frequency, to this*
> *Pure Positive Energy, you'll be inspired through your*
> *path of least resistance.*
>
> ~Abraham-Hicks, excerpted from Asheville, NC
> 4/3/16

The Path of Least Resistance

The path of least resistance is a very important concept to understand in terms of your body, your food and your life in general. Abraham talks about how your Inner Being knows everything you want or have ever wanted. Your Inner Being is also aware of the beliefs and stories you've created during the course of your life that prevent what you want from manifesting in your physical experience. The good news is your Inner Being can lead you to your desires via the path of least resistance despite your opposing beliefs.

In other words, your Inner Being is always guiding you to what you want via the easiest path, not the hardest. It finds a way to communicate with you through the cracks of your resistance, offering you guidance in the way of nudges and ideas, suggestions from other people, quotes on Facebook, a sentence in a magazine, clues for your next steps. Things are happening for you, even when you are unwittingly doing your best to block them. It might not always seem this way, and you might not always understand it, but the more you trust and follow your intuition and the various clues, the more you begin to appreciate how the Universe is orchestrating things in your favor.

To relate this to food, it helps to understand that though you might want to manifest changes in your body, you may question why your intuition is guiding you to eat a gooey piece of baklava, for instance. The thing is, your Inner Being knows the path of least resistance for you. Perhaps the baklava is the thing that will bring you the most comfort in that moment. If you aspire to eat foods you believe to be much healthier than baklava, then focus on seeing yourself eating and enjoying those foods while learning how to be kind to yourself when you don't.

For a very long time, Sheila wanted to eat what she considered a healthy diet, but she kept eating what she believed to be a not-so-healthy diet. What was she focusing on? The fact that she kept eating "the wrong foods." Eventually Sheila began to focus on the body she wanted, and things began to change. She visualized herself looking the way she wanted to look and enjoying a healthy lifestyle. She never got anywhere focusing on "the problem" or the "what is." All that did was put her on a perpetual merry-go-round of disappointment and self-judgement. She accepted the "what is" and learned to love her current body, while also learning how to visualize the transformations she wanted to see in her body.

It really all comes down to this question: what are you focusing on? What are you giving your attention to? Because whatever it is, that's what you're going to continue experiencing.

Many believe that Source is outside of them and that you are separate from Source and being tested in some way. But only you can cause the feeling of separation from Source. That is what all negative emotion is. Source is never withholding from you. Source is always focused upon you, surrounding you with appreciation and unspeakable love.

~Abraham-Hicks, excerpted from Long Beach, CA 9/21/02

Meditation: Tapping into Your All-Knowingness

Meditation helped me become calm under stress. I come from a very anxious family (again, that's just "a story"). If the car or a washing machine needed fixing, it was usually cause for my parents to panic. I picked up on those behaviors and would react with fear whenever I was faced with a challenge—big or small. Abraham's teachings, along with meditation, helped me become more relaxed in the face of a problem. This calmness allows me to live a much more enjoyable and low-stress life. However, many people say they have difficulty meditating. This is understandable.

> Not everyone can sit cross legged on the floor and meditate. I am one of those people. I love to do walking meditations. It's the way I feel connected to my Inner Being. It's my quiet time. After a walk in the woods or by the water, I'll usually come away with an insight, inspiration or answer to a question I've been pondering. As a single mother, it's easy to skip meditation, but I don't because I find it so important to my well-being.
> **—Laura**

The world we live in is fast-paced and full of distractions. Allocating even 10 minutes to sitting quietly when those 10 minutes could be spent folding laundry, returning texts or simply relaxing might be difficult to justify. That is, until you understand the benefits of meditation. Once you grasp how instrumental meditation is in not only creating what you desire, but tapping into an infinite pool of fresh-minded clarity, you will strongly consider setting those 10 or 15 minutes aside each day to meditate in a way that works best for you.

Meditation Helps You Connect with Your True Self

Meditation helps you shatter the illusion that you are disconnected from your Inner Being. This connection provides you with a confidence that is less vulnerable to the world's influences, judgments and expectations, as well as to your own self-judgments. When you meditate, you have more access to who you really are. You tap into that intuitive knowing that you are much more than your physical body, and you gain a deeper relationship with your Inner Being. This relationship enables you to avail yourself of your Inner Guidance. As a result, you are better able to navigate your life experiences in a joyful way. (Who doesn't want more of that?)

Meditation Helps You Fill the Void

Whether aware of it or not, we all want to connect with our Inner Being. We crave it every day. Sometimes we don't quite know how to make this connection and as a result, we feel a void inside us. When we experience this void, we may turn to food or other substances to feel better in an attempt to mimic the experience of alignment. This is not bad or wrong, but it is helpful to know what you can do about it. Meditation is one of the most powerful ways to fill this void. It doesn't mean you'll stop enjoying food or anything else you've grown to love. It means you'll look to these things less to fill a void because you will be filled with a feeling of love, satisfaction and connection to your Inner Being.

Meditation Helps You Attract What You Want

When you meditate, you become a cooperative component to your own good. Through your spiritual connection, you clear the path for the Law of Attraction to work its magic and send you what it knows you want, even if you have forgotten exactly what that is.

When you meditate regularly, there is often a knowing that begins to grow inside you that cannot be described in words. It is a sense of wisdom and peace you may not remember experiencing before. Of course, you have always had access to this knowing. This clarity is priceless and will keep enhancing your life every time you meditate. This deeper relationship with who you really are also helps you to attract what you want (instead of what you don't want), such as the body and life you desire.

Embrace silence since meditation is the only way to truly come to know your source.

~Wayne Dyer, author of
Change Your Thoughts – Change Your Life

There are Many Ways to Meditate

There are countless books, audios and videos on meditation. The key is to begin experimenting and finding what works for you. Abraham suggests focusing on something such as a sound (white noise, for instance) or even the hum of an air conditioner. You may find that focusing on something visual, such as the flame of a candle, is better for you. Currently I like listening to a beautiful piece of music while I focus on my breathing. I notice my thoughts, and every time they pull me away, I bring my attention back to my breathing.

Some people enjoy walking meditations. I live by the Smoky Mountains, so it is a perfect place to take a quiet walk and meditate with nature. Singing and chanting is another way to meditate. If you are new to meditation, you can try sitting quietly for five minutes and slowly build up to 10 or 15 minutes when you're ready. My meditation practices have evolved over the years, and I believe they will continue to do so, just as your spiritual practices will continue to evolve as well.

When to Meditate

I have adopted Abraham's suggestion to meditate as soon as I wake in the morning. I simply roll over (unless I need to hit the restroom first) and turn on a 15-minute piece of meditative piano music. Again, the key is to find what works for you.

Make a decision and then make the decision right. Line up your energy with it. In most cases, it doesn't really matter what you decide. Just decide. There are endless options that would serve you enormously well, and all or any one of them is better than no decision.

~Abraham-Hicks, excerpted from Orlando, FL
2/21/98

Choosing an Eating Style That Feels Good to You

If you are wondering what kind of eating style you should choose, your Inner Being has heard your inquiry. (It's not necessary that you choose an eating style. I don't have a particular eating style per se. But some people feel more comfortable having some sort of plan). Your work is to get in alignment and wait for the answer. However, sometimes the answers don't come as fast as you would like. As a result, you might be thinking, "What do I do in the meantime? I still have to eat." When you read the stories in Part Two of this book, you will learn about each woman's individual journey on the path to trusting her Inner Guidance when it comes to food and her body. While you may not relate to everyone's story, you will begin to get ideas about what could work for you.

The most important thing is to keep following your guidance when it comes to food and everything else in your life. Keep making feeling good your number one priority. Then begin a dialogue with your Inner Being about what kind of eating style would be a good fit for you. Know the answer is coming, and you are always being guided. Your food choices may not always look the way you think they "should," but learning to trust yourself and your body will give you a new relationship with food that is freeing and pleasurable. As I've mentioned before, trust is a big part of the process—trusting your body and trusting yourself. When you're hungry, ask your body, "What do you want right now?"

How would you live your life if you knew you were being guided?

Gabby Bernstein, author of *Super Attractor*

Inner Being, How Can I Look at This Differently?

Your body may want a salad. Or sometimes your body may want something your brain thinks "you shouldn't eat," like a frosted donut. When this happens, ask your Inner Being for guidance, and if you still want the donut, trust it will all be okay.

A few months ago, my husband came home with two desserts for me: a cheese Danish and a chocolate eclair from the best bakery in all of Asheville. It was about 1pm, and I hadn't eaten breakfast. I was quite hungry. Before I knew it, both desserts were gone, having disappeared into my tummy. I basically inhaled them. They were amazing, but afterwards I felt bloated and disappointed with myself.

I was scheduled to sing my first solo the next day at the Center for Spiritual Living in Asheville, and I felt fat because I ate those desserts. Suddenly, the last thing I wanted to do was get up on stage in front of 150 people and sing a solo for the first time in my entire life. I felt ill-at-ease due to my remorse for having eaten those two desserts. In just an instant, I was back to feeling fat and ashamed of my weight. I had to do something to shift my thoughts because I wanted to give a good performance the next day. I wanted to inspire people, but how could I do that if I was feeling so down about myself? I decided to ask my Inner Being for help.

"Inner Being, can you help me look at this differently? I would very much like to have a shift in my energy and the way I'm seeing myself. Help me see this situation the way you see it. Help me see myself the way you see me. I would like to stop torturing myself about having eaten those two desserts. I want to feel confident. I want to get back to feeling beautiful."

I continued talking to my Inner Being that night, and eventually my energy did shift. I began to think of things to appreciate about my body.

I started replacing negative thoughts about myself with positive ones. By the time I woke up the next morning, I was feeling good about myself again, focused on how I could contribute to others with my song.

The point is to get in alignment (feeling emotionally good) as best you can before, during and after you eat. This is more important than what you actually eat, because as we've discussed, your vibration trumps what foods you put in your mouth. Your vibration is the most important factor. As you follow the steps in this book, your relationship with your Inner Being will deepen, and you will know you have access to divine guidance any time you want it.

There is not something you're supposed to do. There's not something that you should do. There is only that which you are inspired to do. And how do you get inspired except by the contrast? It's the life experience that gives you the idea of the desire, and then as you focus upon the desire, the energy flows.

~Abraham-Hicks, excerpted from Philadelphia, PA 4/14/98

When Choosing an Eating Style, Work with Your Beliefs, Not Against Them

As we discussed in Step 3, your beliefs determine your reality. This is why it is so important you work with your beliefs when choosing an eating style. If you believe there is no reason for you to choose an eating style because your body will tell you what it wants/needs, then that is what you should do. If you believe Keto would work for you because it's a good choice for your personality and lifestyle, then that is probably a good choice for you. If you believe Keto would never work for you, then it's pointless to even try it. If you believe any kind of diet or restriction is detrimental to your sanity, then by all means, follow your heart.

Some women I interviewed (as mentioned in Step 4) were guided to join weight-loss groups, others were guided to follow Paleo and yet others were guided to become vegetarians or vegans. In addition, others have been guided to eat what would simply be considered a very "clean" diet in today's parlance. However, what they all have in common is a belief that their chosen eating style will work for them. They also all wanted it to be easy. They were no longer interested in restricted diets that made them feel deprived or anything that didn't feel good. Further, if any of them wanted to have something they considered "unhealthy," they learned how to savor it without guilt.

Your Eating Style May Change Over Time

It is important to know that it is likely your eating style *and* lifestyle will change over time. For instance, I eventually wanted more salads and fewer sweets. I was also inspired to increase my water intake, attend Pilates classes and hike more. The inspiration to eat cleaner and become more active was always there, but once I built more momentum toward being in alignment, it became increasingly easier to do the things I always wanted to do. It is not a matter of willpower for me. It's a matter of ease and flow. Before, I would use food and TV to numb myself as a substitute for finding better-feeling thoughts. I am now more in tune with the inspiration I receive, and my alignment allows me to follow what is calling me.

Bottom line: There is not one eating style that is right for every person. You are a unique individual with unique likes and dislikes, beliefs and experiences, so it is important to trust the guidance *you* are receiving. It's important to trust yourself.

The Law of Attraction Speeds Up Your Momentum

As I explained in Step 1, like attracts like. Simply put, when you think good-feeling thoughts about your body and your food, you attract more good-feeling thoughts about your body and your food. This helps you build even more momentum. Like the snowball rolling downhill, your momentum will build with every better-feeling thought because it is also accumulating other good-feeling thoughts through the Law of Attraction.

Remember, the Law of Attraction works the same way with negative thoughts. However, you are the captain of your ship. You get to choose which thoughts will gain the momentum, so it makes sense to begin the practice of self-soothing, visualizing and all the other practices mentioned in this book. This is how you build momentum toward self-love, body-love and body transformation—or anything else you desire, for that matter.

There are No Wrong Choices and You Can't Make Any Mistakes

You really can't make a wrong choice because there are no wrong choices. You will find you will keep tweaking things as you progress, so if you choose an eating style that doesn't feel right, you can simply try something else. It is often by trial-and-error that you will find what works for you.

> I got up to over 300 pounds. I decided to change my life. I started meditating and listening to my body. It was easier for me to work with my beliefs, so that's what I did. I lost over 70 pounds. Over time, I began adding more "healthy" foods into my diet. Foods I never ate before. I kept meditating, visualizing and listening to Abraham videos. We are all different and I think you have to follow the guidance that is unique to you.
> **—Morgan**

I tried gluten-free at first and had success with that. Then I took it a step further and tried Keto. I liked Keto but found I didn't like having so many rules to follow. So now I simply practice Inspired Eating—I eat what I am inspired to eat. For a time, I incorporated intermittent fasting into my life. I now lean toward eating plant-based foods. I also find enjoyable ways to exercise.

Again, whether you want to manifest changes to your body or simply learn to love the one you have, it's your choice. However, loving yourself and your body can only come when you practice alignment. Once you are more consistently in alignment (a feel-good frame of mind), your inspiration will take you on all sorts of joy-filled journeys regarding your body, your food and your life.

Manifesting your perfect weight is simply a natural result of realigning with your true self.

~Marianne Williamson, author of
A Course in Weight Loss

Allowing vs. Forcing

Allowing: In the allowing model, there is no failure. There are no good or bad foods, and there are no good or bad behaviors. There is only allowing.

When we ***allow*** what we want to flow into our life, such as a more loving relationship with our body and our food, we can picture ourselves standing on a hilltop with open arms or lying on our bed with our palms facing upwards, allowing our good to flow into our experience. We are literally in receiving mode.

Imagine what it would feel like to accept and love your current body, as well as open up to manifesting your new body, whatever that looks like to you. Imagine being open to receiving a new love and appreciation for the physical vessel that is carrying you through this lifetime. Imagine being open to receiving and appreciating your current health, flexibility, longevity and unique beauty—no matter what its current state.

With arms open wide, imagine allowing all your good into your life. Your relationships, your abundance, your health, your experiences...your body. Allow the image you have in your mind of how you would like to look, how you would like to feel, how you would like to dress, how you would like to fit into your clothes to permeate your thoughts. See the image in your mind's eye manifesting into physical

115

existence. You see it, you feel it and you allow it. Over time, the picture in your mind does indeed materialize into your physical experience.

Forcing: On the flip side, think about trying to force those same desired results into existence. That same image you have in your mind of how you would like your body to look, how you want your body to feel, how you would like to dress, how you would like to fit into your clothes—see the image in your mind and instead of *allowing* it to manifest into your physical existence, see yourself trying to force it.

You commit to this way of eating or that way of eating and impose strict rules on yourself. You criticize yourself repeatedly when you fail to stick to those rules. You force yourself to go to the gym and hate every minute of it instead of going when it feels right and enjoying the opportunity to move your body. You try to force yourself to love your body, but all you do is focus on its (perceived) flaws.

We all know too well what forcing ourselves to do something feels like. It feels like a recipe for a whole lot of guilt and shame. We've been sold a bill of goods that taking action is the answer to everything. While taking action seems like common sense, we have been missing an important part of the puzzle. ***Guidance.*** So we force ourselves to take actions that don't feel good and wait impatiently for a reward that never comes. We've been taught if we do not take massive action to solve challenges, we are lazy or somehow damaged.

There's nothing wrong with action. However, when taking action comes from a place of inspiration instead of a place of exerting effort, it's more powerful than you can possibly imagine. Trying to force certain behaviors is the opposite of following your guidance. Following your guidance is all about getting quiet and peaceful enough to hear those little nudges from your Inner Being.

In Part Two, you'll encounter women who share how following their guidance led them to allow what they wanted to flow into their lives, including releasing 25 to 140 pounds each. More important, they experienced joy and self-love as they stopped trying to force themselves to adhere to diets and restrictions that simply didn't work for them.

Love Notes

Tiffany Meditation keeps me tuned into my Inner Being. If you have a hard time with meditation, think "quiet time." Find a way to walk in silence or sit by the ocean. There's no right way to meditate.

Wendy Forcing yourself to eat a certain way is not a good plan for long-term success. Inspired action is a much better plan.

Sylvia These diet programs are all missing the spiritual aspect.

Vivian I wanted to lose weight and I wanted it to be easy. That means I was going to have to call in something bigger than my human self.

Kyle Picture whatever it is you want and feel it. Live it! Become it! I lost 60 pounds and have maintained this weight for over a year. It was easy, because of my focus and attention.

Andrea I let Source guide me to the "diet" that was best for me. I didn't rush it.

Heather I got quiet and listened. I slowed down. I breathed. And the answers came.

Tracy I love myself and I love my life and I love my body. That is the gift of practicing what Abraham-Hicks teaches.

Melinda I can relax about food now. I can make choices that feel good to me. I have stopped the inner critics by replacing them with inner cheerleaders.

Deanna I don't really have a particular way of eating. Instead, I listen to my body and let it tell me what it wants.

Kristen There's nothing wrong with wanting to lose weight. And there's nothing wrong with wanting to stay fat. The real question is, what do YOU want?

Love Your Body Exercises

LOVE YOUR BODY EXERCISE #5.1

Allowing Your Inner Guidance

Part A

Look at the different areas in your life *(see list of areas below)* and ask: Where in my life am I forcing action instead of allowing guidance? **Write your answers in your journal.**

- Relationships
- Health
- Body Image
- Money
- Career/Business

EXAMPLES:

In my relationship with my daughter, I am trying to force an outcome instead of allowing things to unfold.

I find myself trying to force myself to eat things I don't want to eat because they are "healthy."

I often will start an argument with my husband over money.

Part B

Next, write down in your journal how you could handle those situations differently next time they arise.

EXAMPLES:

I can meditate every day for 15 minutes so when I am faced with a challenge with my daughter, I can remain calm and stop trying to control the outcome.

I can practice asking my body what it wants to eat when I'm hungry and trust the answers I receive.

I can write an appreciation list about my life to help me feel more abundant and prosperous. (This will lessen my fear, which is usually the catalyst for starting an argument with my husband over money).

From alignment your body is going to crave what it needs. It's not something you have to force.

~Gianna Rackham, Soul Relationship Coach

LOVE YOUR BODY EXERCISE #5.2

Inner Being Meditation

NOTE: There's no right or wrong way to do this exercise. However you experience this meditation is perfect.

Set aside five to 15 minutes in a quiet place where you won't be interrupted and listen to relaxing music you enjoy. You can set a timer if you like. Place a pen and paper (or your journal) next to you in case you have any insights you want to write down after the meditation.

Get into a comfortable position. You can sit in a chair, cross legged on the floor or lie down on your bed *(whatever works for you)*.

Start the music and close your eyes. While the music is playing, begin to focus on your breathing. Once you are relaxed, start a dialogue with your Inner Being, asking it how it sees you. Don't worry if your mind starts to meander. That's what minds do. Just observe your thoughts and bring your attention back to your breathing.

If you are a visual person, you might want to focus on a beautiful garden or some other pleasant image that comes to mind. Just let things flow while asking to connect with your Inner Being. Ask if your Inner Being has a message for you. Let the dialogue take on a life of its own. Go with the flow. See what you are guided to ask. Perhaps you will be guided to simply listen to the music.

When you are ready to wrap up, simply go back to focusing on your breathing again. Think about any message you received and open your eyes when you are ready.

If you have received a message from your Inner Being, write it down in your journal.

It's okay if you are not aware of any messages. The important thing is to keep meditating. People experience meditation in many ways, but there are almost always eventual benefits from quieting your mind that will enrich your life immensely.

PART TWO
The 25 Stories

Carole's Story
Comfortable in Your Own Skin

*Stop believing your body is against you and
start realizing you're a team. Once you develop that synergy,
then you can begin to trust each other.*

Carole, 53, had always been thin growing up. In fact, she'd been teased throughout school because of it. The other kids called her names like Skinny Minnie, Beanpole and String Bean. Even after the birth of her two children, Carole quickly bounced back to her slender body. She ate what she wanted, exercised several times a week and that was pretty much the extent of her thoughts around weight. That is, until her early forties.

When she met her husband, Roger, Carole was at her ideal weight. But during their first couple of years of dating, she gained 10 pounds. Roger and Carole joked it was her "happy weight," as her pre-Roger life was filled with drama and stress. The stress didn't go away when they married, but Carole found great comfort in her relationship with Roger. They were both incredibly supportive and encouraging of each other's growth. However, the emotional challenges of opening her new massage and bodywork practice caused her to gain more weight.

Even though Carole was manifesting the things she always wanted, such as a successful business and a loving family, the pounds continued to accumulate. And as her weight climbed, she reacted the way society had taught her to react. She dieted. In fact, she tried many diets, but her weight wouldn't budge. Desperate, she consulted her doctor, but he couldn't find any reason for the weight gain.

After a few months, Carole called it quits and decided to do her best to accept the fact that she was simply a bigger woman. And that's when things got worse. Carole became her own personal bully. Each time she saw herself in the mirror, especially a full-length one, she'd say the most horrific things to herself. She dimmed her own light and let her weight define who she was. Carole became a hermit, declining social invitations and saying no to all the things she loved doing with friends. She quit everything that once brought her joy because she was so uncomfortable in her own skin.

Something had to give. One day, Carole asked the "Big U" (Universe) to help her figure out how to lose weight. Soon after, during one of her daily meditations, she caught a glimpse of how her feelings of unworthiness had affected her over the years. Feeling a tiny bit of hope creep in, Carole continued to ask and wait for more guidance during her meditations. She soon received another message: Her first step was to learn how to love and accept her body as is. That was a big aha! moment for Carole. Over time, she began to re-direct her thoughts to those that were loving and accepting of her body—instead of judgmental and critical.

"It's about accepting yourself where you are," says Carole. "That's the beginning of the transformation. And it took me so long to wrap my head around that—that accepting my body, as it is now, is the key to loving myself without any conditions. Accepting where I am, and at the same time, allowing myself the opportunity to expand and change is the key."

As a student of the Law of Attraction, Carole realized that the next step was to start focusing on what she wanted instead of what she didn't want. (For instance, focusing on having a fit, healthy body rather than focusing on how much she hated being overweight.) Once she began to do these two things: 1) accept and love her body as is, and 2) focus on what she wanted instead of what she didn't want, everything began to change. Her body began to release the excess weight—over 50 pounds in one year.

This newfound acceptance of her body and weight created an environment for her body to return to the size that pleased her. And now, when she passes a mirror, she stops and tells herself things like...

I love you!
You're so beautiful!
You're an amazing woman!
You deserve to have it all!
You are worthy!

As Carole began the journey of loving herself, she started asking her body, "What is it that you need?" She developed, as she calls it, a friendship with her body. "I started to ask my body questions and as a result of listening to the answers, I began to change my entire way of eating," shares Carole. "And it was easy. It wasn't this big event. I didn't sit down and say, okay, I'm going to eat this, this and this. Or I'm going to follow this diet or that diet. I just started asking, in the moment, what I should eat, what my body wanted, and I started listening."

"Intuitive eating for me goes something like this," continues Carole. "When I'm hungry, I'll think, what is it I really want? Sometimes it's a piece of cheese. And if it's something that used to be a binge food for me, like candy, I will look deeper into that, and I'll ask myself, why are you wanting candy? I realized, in many cases, it was simply a habit. Other times I found I needed an energy boost, or maybe I was feeling a little down. Sometimes I was feeling sad because my husband left for a business trip. And so I started becoming mindful about my eating and just asking a few questions. And if I did wind up eating the candy, I didn't beat myself up about it like I used to."

"The beauty of this process," Carole explains, "is that I started craving healthier and healthier things. As I played with this asking technique, my body would start asking for healthy but strange combinations. For instance, all of a sudden I got this craving for sautéed mushrooms and kale over rice. I never had that in my life! I didn't even know how to make it, but I figured, I'll just throw some oil and garlic in the pan and sauté them up. I also started paying more attention to my hunger. More and more I ate only when I was hungry. I noticed there were times I wanted to eat three times a day and some days I felt very hungry and ate six times a day. Other days, I wasn't hungry at all and ate very little. I learned to get in tune with my body and trust its signals. In one year of listening to my body, I dropped 35 pounds."

Carole now spends time each day feeding her spirit with positive self-talk—loving words that honor her and highlight her worth. She also meditates and visualizes daily, seeing her future self and deeply connecting with the feeling of once again having her ideal body and experiencing the freedom of feeling lighter. She's so happy to feel more comfortable in her own skin and to learn to love herself no matter what her weight. No more diets, no more brutal workouts—just simple, healthy eating and exercises she enjoys.

Carole's 5 Steps

STEP 1
Love and Accept Yourself Where You Are
The first step is truly accepting yourself where you are. You may not be at a weight you are happy about. You may have 20, 30, 40, 100 or even more pounds you want to release, but until you love and accept where you are, it's difficult to move forward

STEP 2
Change Your Inner Dialogue About Your Body
Almost every woman I've ever talked to has abused herself because of her weight: verbally and with her thoughts. Most women who want to release pounds aren't kind to themselves. So the second step is shifting that behavior and becoming friends with your body. Begin a love affair with yourself. Start out by catching yourself thinking or saying negative things about yourself or your body and replace those thoughts with positive ones.

It's important to say things you can believe. If you reach too far, your brain won't buy it. So, start out with statements that are a little bit softer, such as "I know I'm not where I want to be, but I love and accept myself anyway," or "I know I just ate all those cookies, but I'm going to try and love and accept myself anyway," and work your way up to even more powerful statements you can align with such as, "You are beautiful!" "I love you." "My body is amazing as is and getting more beautiful all the time!"

STEP 3
Ask Your Body What It Wants to Eat
Once you start accepting your body as is and transforming the way you talk and think about your body, you're now ready to start experimenting with listening to what your body needs and wants...and trusting the messages you receive. You may be guided to try a certain food plan, or you may be guided to practice intuitive eating without any sort of plan. Everyone is different. Trust and follow the guidance you're receiving about next steps. And remember, these steps are more than likely going to fly in the face of what the diet industry tells you to do, and that's okay.

STEP 4
Meditate
An important part about listening to your body is tapping into your true self, your higher self, your God/Goddess or whatever you want to call it. (Abraham calls it your Inner Being.) It's how you get in touch with your intuition. It's how you can receive the messages from your body and your higher self. You have to be able to quiet your mind so you can tap into your soul powers and wisdom. Without taking five, 10, 15 minutes a day to quiet your mind, it's a lot more difficult to receive these messages and communicate with your body. Meditation is key to not only physical wellness but spiritual growth.

STEP 5
Visualize
Do not underestimate the power of this step! I couldn't be where I am today without it. It is extremely powerful. Visualize yourself at the weight you want to be. Visualize yourself going into your closet, for example, and picking out a nice new pair of jeans at the size you want to be. Feel those jeans easily slipping up over your legs and zipping up

over your tummy smoothly and effortlessly. Imagine the emotions you will feel when this happens. Imagine the satisfaction, the joy, the happiness. Feel those feelings now. (It's so important to feel the feelings in the present during the visualization.) Five minutes a day is all you need, and it will change your life!

Morgan's Story
Accepting Your Current Body First

The challenge isn't about losing weight. It's about accepting who you are and where you are and from there, creating whatever you want.

Morgan remembers the incident with her classmate like it was yesterday. She was 10 years old, and the young girl called her fat. Morgan surprised herself when she fired back, "No, *you're* fat." She surprised herself even more when she asked a random boy in the schoolyard which girl was fatter. The boy ran off, leaving the two girls to figure it out for themselves.

That wasn't the first time someone had mentioned her size. Two years earlier, the family physician told Morgan's mother, "If she continues to grow like this, she'll become obese."

During college was the first time Morgan lived away from home, and she could now eat whatever she wanted. (Her mom cooked all her meals when she lived at home.) With no restraint, Morgan proceeded to eat everything in sight. Pizza, hot dogs, ice cream, candy—she would eat whatever she could get her hands on. Every month the money on her meal card ran out early.

In college, Morgan also began to try various diets and fitness programs. "One was crazier than the next," she shares. "P90X, the GM diet, Atkins, the Apple Cider Vinegar Diet and more. All of them were good for losing a pound or two, but I could never complete them. I got to the point where I decided I would rather be fat and happy. The only problem was, I wasn't happy." By the time Morgan graduated from college, she was 300 pounds.

Throughout life, including after college, Morgan hid her body in baggy jeans and T-shirts, even though the loose clothes made her look larger. She avoided wearing shorts and didn't go to the gym because she was embarrassed and felt that everyone was judging her. Eventually her weight held her back in business. As a freelance graphics designer, she found herself reluctant to go out to meet clients.

Frustrated with her size, Morgan tortured herself with endless questions:

Why do I turn to food for comfort?
Why am I doing this to myself?
Why can't I treat myself better?

When Morgan, 29, was living in Charlotte, NC, she hired a business coach. The coach took her to a personal development course that started her on a path of what she calls a "spiritual awakening." The course, along with a breakup with her long-time boyfriend, led her to the discovery of the Law of Attraction. In a nutshell, the Law of Attraction says our thoughts create our reality.

Around this time, Morgan landed a large website design project, which was an exciting achievement. However, she found herself struggling with the design and soon realized she felt blocked because the website was about health. The subject matter "was in her face," so to speak. Her coach, sensing Morgan wanted a breakthrough with her weight, suggested she create a health challenge for herself including a vision of what she wanted her body to look like and even more: what she wanted her life to look like. They talked about what Morgan wanted one, two and five years down the road, and then her coach asked her the magic question...

"What would your life look like if you loved yourself?"

"The challenge really wasn't about losing weight," Morgan shares. "It was about loving who you are and where you are. It was about self-acceptance." Her coach suggested the changes in her body would come naturally and easily once she learned how to love and accept herself.

During the challenge, Morgan discovered the teachings of Abraham-Hicks and learned about the power of beliefs. She discovered not only do our thoughts create our reality, our beliefs create our reality (what we manifest into existence) as well. This revelation caused her to examine her ideas about food and weight and to realize she believed certain foods made her fat.

Soon Morgan found herself inspired to create an eating style in which she would avoid the foods she believed made her gain weight or that didn't agree with her. There weren't many of them, and this left her with a wide variety of other foods to eat. She didn't set up a strict regimen by any means. If she found herself eating a food that was on her "avoid list," she learned how to soothe herself about it. She didn't make a big deal out of it. She simply went back to eating the foods that she believed agreed with her body (and wouldn't make her fat—as per her beliefs) as soon as she could.

This didn't feel like deprivation to Morgan. She had tried "deprivation diets" before, as mentioned above, and they never worked for her. Avoiding these foods (for the most part) felt different because she was "working with her beliefs, not against them." She believed when she ate specific foods, she would gain weight, so why not sidestep those foods and see what happens?

The experiment showed promise immediately, and Morgan began to release pounds. She also decided to add one food each week that she believed would help her reach her goals. For instance, one week she added a new vegetable to her diet. The next week she added a fruit, and so on. She followed her Inner Guidance concerning each choice. If she liked it, she continued eating it a few times during the week. If she didn't like it, she wouldn't eat it again.

Morgan also added meditation to her daily routine. She received so many benefits from meditation that it became a big part of her life. She reached the point where she wanted to start every day with that practice. In addition, Morgan began complimenting herself. She would tell her legs, "You're beautiful." She would talk to her stomach, "Are those core muscles I see there?" When she looked in the mirror, she would say, "You are looking sexy today!" Morgan eventually felt inspired to begin walking every day, listening to spiritual, educational and inspirational books during her walks. It's what she enjoys and looks forward to the most.

Over the past year, Morgan has lost a total of 74 pounds. She started out at a size 24 at 300 pounds and is now a size 18 and weighs 226 pounds. She envisions celebrating her 34th birthday next year by slipping into a size 16 and expects to ultimately reach her target weight of 150 pounds. More important than releasing pounds, Morgan shares how she learned to love herself and believes this self-love is the key to transforming her body.

Morgan's 5 Steps

STEP 1
Meditate Daily

Meditation is about connecting to the person you are—your true self. It may seem unrelated to loving your body or releasing pounds, but the opposite is true. It's everything. If you want a huge advantage in creating what you want, begin to meditate—even if it's for 10 minutes a day. When you meditate, you connect with incredible power and clarity, enabling you to accomplish things that previously seemed impossible.

STEP 2
Create a Vision

Create a vision of what you want your body and your life to look like and a target date for manifestation. It's okay if you don't achieve the vision by the date specified. The important thing is to create the image and focus on it every day. Add as much feeling and detail as possible (as long as it feels good to do so) to make the vision come alive—so it feels tangible. See it, feel it, taste it and touch it!

STEP 3
Practice Self-Love and Self-Acceptance

You take care of your car. You take it to be serviced. Why not take care of your body too? Compliment yourself. Love yourself. Take care of you. Accept where you are. Accept your current body. As long as you are hating your current body, it will be impossible to make progress toward change. When we hate our bodies, all we end up doing is sabotaging our efforts. Accept where you are and begin the journey of loving yourself—including your body!

STEP 4
Listen to Your Body
Your body is always telling you something. Are you listening? It's easier to listen when you are calm. Meditation will help with that. Your body tells you what it wants to eat. It tells you when it needs rest. It tells you when it's thirsty. It tells you when it wants to move. What is your body saying to you? You'll have to get quiet and listen to find out.

STEP 5
Have Fun!
I found listening to books while walking to be fun. What is fun for you? What makes your heart sing? If you're not sure, find out and then do that! Fun is the secret sauce that brings everything you want to you. It's so simple yet few people know of its power. Make no mistake—enjoying life will work wonders!

Tiffany's Story
On the Run to Self-Love

I had to learn that it's okay for me to like myself.
It's okay to think of myself as beautiful.

Tiffany's childhood was far from typical. In fact, you could say she grew up on the run, which is exactly what she relates in her autobiographical book, *Insane Roots*. The book follows the life of a criminal and her unsuspecting daughter. As you might guess, Tiffany is the daughter. Her mom regularly moved them from city-to-city throughout Tiffany's childhood due to crimes that included check fraud, fake deposits, identity theft, grand theft auto and more. They were often broke. Tiffany, 37, remembers sleeping in the car with her mom on many occasions because they had no money for a hotel room, let alone an apartment.

Her mom was in and out of jail, and at times Tiffany was placed in foster care. When Tiffany was 10, her foster care family (who knew her since she was a toddler and who eventually became her godparents) took her to Wisconsin to live with her grandparents. The grandparents obtained full custody of her, and Tiffany, 11, finally began to have some stability in her life.

It's no surprise Tiffany's childhood affected her self-esteem and sense of security. Previous unhealthy relationships had become a pattern, and once she started high school, the unhealthy relationships continued. For instance, one boyfriend, who turned out to be an alcoholic, was constantly asking her for money. Another was verbally abusive.

Tiffany fell into what she calls an undesirable lifestyle. Bar food became her dinner and alcohol her daily beverage. That's when she started putting on weight. "If you hang out in Wisconsin bars, you eat a lot of cheese curds and drink a lot of beer," says Tiffany. It got to the point where she couldn't remember the last time she had an alcohol-free day. "I always harbored this abandonment feeling because my mom would disappear for days or weeks at a time when I was young. I kept trying to find that sense of security in others—even if they were a bad influence. A classic case of looking for love in all the wrong places."

Tiffany was often depressed about her weight. By the time she published her book in 2014, she had almost doubled her size to 200 pounds. She was 5' 2" tall and had hovered around 110 pounds in early high school.

"I realize now that I didn't have to be ashamed of my body, but that's how I was feeling back then," she recalls. "I was living in Colorado and basically became a hermit. I didn't want to be seen in public because I felt so unattractive. I wore big dresses to hide my body. I believed people were laughing at me because of my weight. I developed a lot of social anxiety."

Feeling hopeless, Tiffany reached out to her childhood friend Brittany, who now lives in North Carolina. Brittany turned out to be a breath of fresh air. She saw her friend was stuck in a cycle of negativity and wanted to help. During their phone conversations, Brittany mentioned Abraham-Hicks. Tiffany started studying Abraham's teachings and the next week, Brittany mailed Tiffany the Abraham-Hicks DVD, *Think and Grow Slim*. After watching the DVD twice, Tiffany experienced an aha! moment: "My weight is not about my relationship with food. It's about my thoughts. My negative thoughts are causing the weight gain and the depression."

This realization, coming from the discovery of Abraham-Hicks and the reunion with her childhood friend, sparked new hope and confidence. The two friends continued to discuss Abraham-Hicks as Brittany nudged Tiffany toward meditation. At first, Tiffany resisted because her "brain goes a million miles a minute." She didn't think she could sit quietly long enough to meditate. Brittany reassured her that meditation is the way to hear the guidance from within, and since Tiffany knew (from listening to Abraham-Hicks) how important it is to connect with her Inner Being, she decided to give it a go. She began with one of the meditations from the *Getting into the Vortex: Guided Meditations CD and User Guide*, per Brittany's suggestion. (These are guided meditations accompanied by music that lead you to focus on your breathing.) Tiffany found she could easily do the 15-minute meditations and actually enjoyed them.

After meditating for a few weeks, Tiffany's next aha! moment came when she realized it was time to change her negative self-talk about her weight. "I knew I needed to accept myself and my body, but it's hard when you've been criticizing yourself for so long." Through trial and error, Tiffany learned she couldn't just get rid of those negative thoughts. She needed to replace them with something new.

She began training her mind to think better-feeling thoughts. "You are beautiful. You are healthy. You are powerful," she would tell herself throughout the day. "In the beginning, I worried about being conceited," says Tiffany. "I was raised to be humble by my godparents and grandparents. I had to learn that it's okay for me to like myself. It's okay to think of myself as beautiful."

The better she became at replacing negative thoughts with positive ones, the more pounds she began to shed. "Every pound I lost was another issue I worked through," explains Tiffany. "And it's not really 'work.' It's learning how to love yourself. It's being kinder to yourself with your self-talk. It's meditating and getting connected with your Inner Being. It's all these things."

Tiffany went on to let go of 70 pounds in 18 months. "I started doing a lot of walking and visualizing myself in the body I wanted as I walked. I never dieted or felt like I was depriving myself of the foods I loved. I ate what I wanted, but the more I changed my thoughts and the more I meditated, the more I craved healthier foods. Eventually I was drawn to a vegetarian way of eating but again, I never said, 'You can't have this and you can't have that.' I ate what I was guided to eat."

Tiffany also stopped weighing herself every day. "As a woman, my body weight fluctuates all the time, so why bother weighing myself? Instead, I taped the number of my goal weight onto the scale. I stepped on the scale every day and pretended I reached that number. I got excited and jumped around, as if it was really happening, and eventually it did."

Today, Tiffany lives in her grandparents' house (they have since passed) with her boyfriend of two years, Michael, "who is a real sweet guy." She is a published author and an entrepreneur, having started her own business in 2019. Her weight is down to 136 pounds, and she continues to study the work of Abraham-Hicks.

Tiffany's 5 Steps

STEP 1
Appreciate the Journey
Find a way to appreciate the positive aspects of your journey, including your weight. Find peace with all of it. Write a list of positive aspects about everything you want to feel better about.

STEP 2
Meditate
Just a few minutes a day of getting quiet and connecting with your Inner Being will change your life.

STEP 3
Accept Yourself Where You Are
Learn to make peace with where you are. Without acceptance, it's difficult to make any changes.

STEP 4
Upgrade Your Thoughts
Stop self-defeating thoughts such as comparing yourself to others. Instead, learn to build yourself up and do what feels good to you. Comparison is a waste of time because you are unique. Practice thinking better-feeling thoughts about yourself, and your life will transform.

STEP 5
Learn to Think About Food Differently
Many of us have been brainwashed to believe food is the enemy. This creates a lot of unnecessary guilt, insecurity and confusion. Food is not the enemy. Learn to love your food by creating a new story about it. Learn to appreciate and love whatever you eat.

Jeana's Story
Breaking the Binge-Eating Cycle

Our diet culture teaches us to feel guilty about eating, and this guilt creates so much shame. I carried this shame for years, and it caused me to go on binge after binge.

Jeana, 53, stumbled upon the teachings of Abraham-Hicks after she set an intention to release 45 pounds. The message she kept hearing in the Abraham audios was: get happy where you are and don't sweat it. So that's exactly what she decided to do. "I did whatever it took to learn to love and accept my current body," she shares. "I did lots of mirror work, telling myself 'I feel beautiful.' I also got rid of my scale because weighing myself created stress. I learned what foods resonated with me and what foods didn't. And if I grabbed something to eat that I used to think was 'bad for me,' I didn't beat myself up about it anymore."

This past year for Jeana has been about listening to her body and getting into alignment. "The more I trusted my body to tell me what it wanted to eat, the more my body eventually wanted what I consider healthy foods." Jeana was also guided to re-join a popular weight-loss program. "This time around, things were much easier," she recalls. "Because of studying Abraham, I know the importance of meditation, visualization and alignment. When I re-joined the weight-loss program, I wanted things to be easy and fun just like Abraham says they're supposed to be. And they were. In 10 months, I lost 40 pounds and it wasn't a struggle like it was 25 years ago. I've gone down four clothing sizes from a 14 to a size six, and it continues to be an enjoyable and enlightening experience."

Jeana started meditating every day, sometimes multiple times a day. In fact, she believes meditation is the most important component of her success. "Meditation allows you to get in tune with your Inner Being so you can hear the messages coming through," she explains. "When I started meditating, I got the impulse to begin walking. I was never a very active person, but I felt a strong urge to move my body. I started hiking up the hill near my house since I live on top of a mountain in Texas Hill Country. Last year, these hills intimidated me, and now they call to me. I look forward to my walks and have built up my stamina. I enjoy nature, and most times it feels like a walking meditation that feeds my soul."

Instead of focusing on losing weight, Jeana looks at her path as a health journey. "That anxious feeling you get when you're trying to lose weight—you beat yourself up if you think you've 'cheated.' You criticize yourself. I didn't do that this time, and I believe that it's the Abraham teachings that have helped me learn to be kinder to myself...be happy where I am. I also believe the vibration of loving yourself helps you metabolize your food in a different way— a way that benefits you more."

During the years that she felt bigger than she wanted to be, Jeana compared herself to other women. She felt envious of anyone with an athletic physique. She hid her body in her clothes and thought many negative thoughts about her appearance. "I always wore long blouses that covered my stomach and thighs," says Jeana. She experienced much self-criticism and believes she used food to feel better. "That's why self-love is the cure. When you learn to love yourself, you don't feel the need to self-medicate with food."

Abraham often mentions there are no good or bad foods, and this helped Jeana reverse her cycle of binge-eating. In the past, the guilt of eating one cookie, for instance, led her to eat many, many more well after she was full. "Our society doesn't buy into the philosophy that there are no good or bad foods, but letting go of this mindset is liberating. Our diet culture teaches us to feel guilty about eating this or that, and this guilt creates so much shame. I carried this kind of shame for so many years, and it made me overeat because I felt so bad about myself. Understanding that self-love keeps us from the need to numb ourselves with food or any other substance is the best kept secret in the world, and I hope the secret gets out."

Jeana's 5 Steps

STEP 1
Love Yourself and Your Body
Learn how to thoroughly enjoy who you are all the way down to your soul and every fiber of your being. Without that piece, you will start a weight-loss journey out of self-hatred instead of self-love. If you are coming from self-hatred, you are likely to gain back any weight you lose. If you are coming from self-love, you are tapped into your Inner Being and will have moments of clarity and inspiration that guide you throughout your life. It's the difference between ease and struggle, allowing guidance or white knuckling it.

STEP 2
Meditate
Meditation is a must if you want to make the process of transforming your body easy and fun. By meditating, you tap into your Inner Being, who will guide you every step of the way. Meditation offers you calmness and confidence. You will receive messages and impulses, telling you when to act. You will begin to trust your intuition more. You will feel less fear and uncertainty in your life in general, and you will begin to know who you really are. Once you know that, it is impossible not to love yourself.

STEP 3
Journal
Journaling is a very powerful tool. Every day, I use my journal to write what Abraham calls "positive aspects"—a list of things I love about myself, my life and my body. This practice helped me change how I feel about myself. I also write down quotes that help me feel good and paste inspiring artwork into my journal. You can write positive aspects

about anything in your journal. I have transformed many aspects of life through writing these lists, including my body.

STEP 4
Visualize

Although I've always visualized, I never realized how life-changing visualization truly is until I started intentionally imagining what I wanted. I have changed my entire world with visualization. The trick is to add the feeling to the process. Most nights before bed, I visualize something I want (for instance, I visualized myself at the size I wanted to be). Once I see the picture in my mind, I feel the feelings of having already manifested it. I get in tune with the vision. I believe it. I make the visualization become so real in my mind that it must happen.

STEP 5
Follow Inspired Action

If you join the gym and your heart's not in it, chances are you won't go for long. If you start any exercise routine and your heart's not in it, you'll find it difficult to follow through. Things are different when you proceed from inspired action. An idea pops into your head, and it feels good. There is no resistance. You are inspired to join the gym, for instance, and then you go when you are inspired to go. You don't beat yourself up when you don't. Instead, you listen within and allow a schedule that's just right for you to establish itself. Keep meditating and listening to your body. When you follow inspired action, your heart is in the thing you choose (whatever it may be), and it will be easy.

Tami's Story
Time to Go Within

*In the past six months, my sugar levels returned
to a normal range, and my doctor has taken me off
insulin and diabetes medication.*

Tami, 61, enjoyed a wonderful childhood growing up all over the country and world. Her father's position as a major in the Marine Corps required the family to move every few years. They lived in over 15 states as well as Austria and Iceland where Tami skied some of the most beautiful mountains in Europe and even a glacier in Iceland. "My dad made everything an adventure," says Tami.

She can't remember ever having negative thoughts about her body until she was 11years old and reached for a second helping of mashed potatoes. "You shouldn't have that," advised her dad. "Have some vegetables instead." Looking back, she knows her dad had good intentions. He himself was required to be thin for his job, as the Marine Corps was very strict about weight. Tami recalls her dad starving himself for weeks in order to make his weight requirement.

When Tami was a teenager, her dad would often wake her up at 6am when it was still dark outside to go jogging with him. "I'm not sure if it was his way of trying to help me get in shape or if he wanted to instill this sense of discipline in me," Tami ponders. "I didn't think too much about it at the time. I got up, got dressed and went jogging."

At age 18, Tami was a size 12-14 and remembers feeling good about her appearance. Things changed when she started dating Caleb. After a few weeks, Caleb told her she was fat. Devastated, Tami proceeded to go on a low-calorie diet. She turned to weight-loss products of the time such as Metrecal and Sego (both popular for their diet shakes). Her mother also got on the diet bandwagon. They ate cottage cheese and bought lots of sugar-free foods. "I often ate one can of soup for the entire day accompanied by a steady flow of diet drinks," Tami recalls.

Caleb and Tami were married the next year, and she gave birth to her first child at 21. "I wasn't happy in the marriage," she shares, "and was under a lot of emotional stress because of the relationship. Even though my husband would complain about my weight, food was the thing that relaxed me. I gained 85 pounds while pregnant." The two stuck it out as long as they could and divorced after 11 years when Tami was 30 and their children were four and eight years old. The next two husbands Tami attracted also complained about her weight before marrying her. At the time of her third divorce, Tami had climbed to 250 pounds.

Throughout the years, Tami kept trying the latest diet. She would lose large amounts of weight and then gain it all back and more. She did Atkins for about a year. While she lost 25 pounds, "It gave you bad breath and left you feeling horrible all the time." Then there was the Suzanne Somers diet, the Richard Simmons exercise and diet programs, the Alkaline diet and more.

Tami was living in Alabama after her third divorce. This last marriage was more chaotic than the other two marriages combined, and she knew it was time to make a change. Several spiritual teachers started showing up in her life, and she began to crave more meaning and joy. Tami realized she had been looking outside herself for guidance, love and validation her entire life. She looked to her father, her husbands, her children and even to her work for answers and meaning. It was time to do things differently, she thought. It was time to look within.

The first change came when she stopped working at home after hours in order to create a new block of time to just "be." (She had previously worked 12-14 hours a day, responding to client texts and preparing contracts at home late at night.) Next, she got rid of the wi-fi, TV and cable in her house. "I used the internet and TV to check out," says Tami. "They helped me ignore my feelings. I guess I was afraid of those feelings." Once these distractions were removed, she found herself asking, "Now what?" The answers trickled in. First came the inspiration to meditate, where she would ask for guidance. "Show me the right teachers. Lead me to my next steps."

Tami soon started reading many spiritual books, including some of the books about the teachings of Abraham-Hicks. She then met a woman who taught her how to let go of the pain she was holding onto— emotional pain, physical pain. "She taught me about journaling. I journaled about what I was experiencing, about what I wanted and about how I wanted to feel. This spiritual teacher instructed me to rip out the pages of my journal at the end of each week and burn them—so that's what I did. After a year of this practice, I felt much lighter. I began to change my beliefs about my relationships as well as about my body and food," Tami continues. "I realized there are no good or bad foods. It's about how I felt when I was eating. In the past, I was completely stressed out when I ate, but I changed all that. I also sat in silence for 15 minutes a day, asking, 'What can I do to bring my body into perfect health?' I visualized how I wanted my life to be, how I wanted to look. I asked what to add to my diet (not what to take away). Eventually I was guided to engage in more self-care and self-love. I got out in nature every day. At least once a month, I did something extraordinary for myself such as get a massage, facial or something else that felt special."

Slowly but surely, without even trying, Tami experienced the pounds coming off, even though she hadn't actually lost any weight yet. She felt it happening before it happened. "I began to visualize myself doing things that are easier with a fit and healthy body, such as hiking in the mountains, global traveling, yoga, walking up the stairs easily and feeling energized and rested when I wake in the morning. As a result of journaling, meditating, visualizing and more, I eventually was guided to buy organic, fresh foods. I felt these foods bringing love and light to my body and my spirit. As I began to eat foods that were infused with sunshine, I could feel myself becoming happier. For 10 months, I ate like that before noticing the weight melting away. Then I bought a scale and watched the numbers go down. 'Everything is always working out for my highest and best,' I would repeat hundreds of times throughout the day. Every morning, I asked, 'What am I supposed to do today?' and I listened to the messages coming from within."

Tami now feels more peaceful than she's ever felt and has transformed her health. "Years ago, I was diagnosed with Type 2 diabetes, fatty liver disease and high blood pressure. It's almost a year since I began eating a plant-based diet. I felt better immediately. My most recent labs showed no indications of a fatty liver. In the past six months, my sugar levels returned to a normal range, and my doctor has taken me off insulin and diabetes medication. I expect to be off my blood pressure medicine in the next few months as well. I've released over 77 pounds. My highest weight was 250 pounds, size 22-24, and now I'm 173 pounds, size 16."

Tami proclaims, "My life is completely different. In fact, it's unrecognizable. I'm being guided to embark upon projects I never dreamed possible, and it's all because of learning how to go within and trust the messages I receive from my Inner Being."

Tami's 5 Steps

STEP 1
Practice Thinking Better-Feeling Thoughts
Before, during and after eating, let go of anything that is making you feel less than great and choose thoughts that feel better.

STEP 2
Embrace Your Inner Being
You are powered by the strongest force in the Universe, always working for your highest and best outcome. Know it. Feel it. Own it.

STEP 3
Stop Criticizing and Complaining
Stop complaining. Period. Stop complaining about your life. Stop complaining about your body. Stop complaining about others. If you like, you can write out your complaints on paper along with other things you want to let go of and burn those papers at the end of each week—or immediately! This technique helped me stop complaining and criticizing myself and others and made me a calmer and happier person.

STEP 4
Meditate
Take 10-15 minutes a day to sit in silence so you can hear the messages from your Spirit Guides, Teachers or Inner Being (use whatever term that works for you). Journal these messages. Many messages also come during your dream state. Keep a dream journal.

STEP 5
Dream Big (Visualize)

Keep a journal of at least 50 things you would like to manifest. Write them all in the form of "I Am" statements. (For example: "I Am feeling healthy and strong." "I Am manifesting money for travel.") Then choose the top five items you would like to focus on for the month. Use a 3x5 card to write these five "I Am" statements on one side. On the back, write five "I Am" statements for things you want to manifest within a year. Laminate the card and carry it around with you so you can keep reviewing it throughout the day. Each month create a new card, making any adjustments necessary.

Diana's Story
What Do You Believe?

*I lost a lot of weight quickly and easily because
I told the story that my body loses weight quickly
and easily. Obviously, you have to tell a story
that's believable and comfortable for you.*

"Food was a big deal in our family," says Diana, who currently lives in New Jersey with her husband and two sons. "Not that there's anything wrong with enjoying food. It's natural. But back then, everything seemed to revolve around it." Food became even more important to a pre-teen Diana when her parents divorced. "My dad would pick us up, take us out to eat and it was a free-for-all. Suddenly there weren't any rules. We could eat whatever and as much as we wanted. I remember going to McDonald's and being allowed to order two Big Macs, a large shake and fries. When I hit 12-13 years of age, I started getting heavy."

While her weight fluctuated from that point on throughout adulthood, Diana, now 45, never felt she struggled with her weight. "I felt concern about my size when I was in middle school and high school, but I always believed I would lose it easily and quickly whenever I chose to and that always happened—because I expected it. Even before I knew about the Law of Attraction and the power of belief, I was living it."

Diana enjoyed a confidence about her body and food that few people wanting to release pounds experience. "When I was heavier, I never felt that my weight got in the way of what I wanted. It never affected my social or professional life. I was always very successful, I had great jobs, lots of friends and no trouble attracting men. I think if I had a belief that being fat would prevent me from getting dates or jobs, like many of my friends did (and still do), that's what I would have created."

Things shifted when Diana saw a photo of herself at her son's christening. "I did not recognize myself," says Diana. "I remember thinking, 'I don't even know who that is.' I didn't feel that big, although my weight had climbed to 258 pounds, the heaviest I've ever been. I gave birth to my son and lost my mother prior to gaining that weight. It was both a wonderful and heart-wrenching time because while I was so happy to have another son, I was devastated to lose my mom."

After seeing that photo, Diana decided to return to a weight-loss program that had always worked for her. At that point, she was just beginning to listen to Abraham-Hicks recordings. She resonated with the teachings because she intuitively knew the important role beliefs play in the achievement of anything. It was a natural evolution for Diana to begin complimenting her program with what she was learning from Abraham. She knew her fitness efforts were going to work because she believed they would work, and Abraham confirmed her philosophy.

In the weight-loss program she re-joined, Diana weighed in every week. She remembers the woman weighing her saying, "Don't worry if you only lose a pound a week." Diana smiled politely but silently told herself, "I'm going to lose two pounds a week," and that's exactly what happened.

162

Diana lost 102 pounds in 51 weeks, and she has kept if off for six years and counting. For some reason, however, she began to experience resistance after losing the first 50 pounds. It stopped being easy. The more she read and listened to Abraham, the more she started asking herself, "Why do I have to work so hard at this? Abraham says it's supposed to be easy and fun." At that point, Diana was going to the gym four or five times a week for an hour each time. She knew she was going to release pounds that way, but it was starting to feel like a chore. And there was Abraham saying she didn't have to struggle. She wanted the process to be enjoyable, just as Abraham said it could be. Diana started to increase her time listening to Abraham audios and videos, and the additional 50 pounds then came off with a fraction of the mental and physical effort. "I was getting amazing results physically, emotionally and spiritually," Diana recalls.

As far as food and exercise were concerned, Diana began following her guidance about her body's desires. "I exercised when it felt good to do so. I tapped into my guidance about what to eat, finding that I wanted to eat fresh and clean during the week, but on the weekends, I was a little looser with my food. My only criterion was that I felt good before, during and after I ate. No guilt or criticizing myself over food choices. I made it a point to eat from a feel-good place."

Generally speaking, Diana no longer weighs herself. "I don't focus on that anymore. I go by how I feel in my body. If I'm feeling heavy in my body, I know what to do. I know how to shift my energy and to ask for guidance as to what's going to bring me back to feeling lighter or more flexible. It's no longer about the number on the scale."

Diana emphasizes the need to find alignment (a place of feeling emotionally good) and from there discover what's going to work for you individually. "You can't expect to have success with what worked for someone else because they are sure to have different beliefs from yours. Your personal beliefs and thought vibration are the most important factors in manifesting anything."

"Also," Diana adds, "if you're having trouble believing you can lose weight, I would suggest two things that will open your mind and assist you: 1) Meditation. Meditation is extremely powerful. It gets you connected to your Inner Being, who knows the truth of who you are and knows that all things are possible. 2) Identify and work with your beliefs. Once you identify your beliefs around food and weight, you can customize a plan that you believe will work for you. I really wouldn't do anything until you believe it will work for you because you're wasting your time. Sometimes not doing anything is doing something."

"For instance," Diana continues, "I believe eating clean and fresh most of the time and indulging on the weekends (or when I want to) works for my body. I also believe that exercising when I'm inspired to do so also works for my body, and as a result of my beliefs, that's exactly what I experience. I'm working with my beliefs, and I'm savoring life based on the path of least resistance. It's a wonderful way to live."

Diana's 5 Steps

STEP 1
Allow the Inspiration to Come Forward

Desire to feel emotionally better. From there, you can begin to practice alignment (soothing yourself when upset and basking in thoughts such as appreciation when you feel good). Don't try to force any behavior or feeling. Instead, learn how to allow things to come to you, including the good feelings that will help you manifest more of what you want. Think of it as receiving inspiration instead of pushing against the flow or bucking the current. To release pounds, ask for inspiration and guidance for what your body wants to eat and how it wants to move in order to achieve this goal. There is no need to rush into action. Practice trusting the guidance you receive.

STEP 2
Appreciate Your Body

Your body is a living, breathing miracle. It can rid itself of ailments ranging from a paper cut to cancer. It can accept organs from other beings and thrive. It can make babies from scratch generally through a quite pleasurable act. Your cells regenerate constantly. Your heart is pumping blood around the clock. Your lungs cleanse the air you breathe, and you have an intelligent brain to orchestrate the entire show. Your body performs billions of other functions that keep your amazing machine running smoothly day-in and day-out. Even if you can't appreciate your body because you think it's too fat or because it has stretch marks, cellulite, warts or whatever, find *something* good to notice about your physical self and show it some love. Give your body positive reinforcement, and it will *always* yield more aspects to feel positive about.

165

STEP 3
Work with Your Beliefs

The main reason heavy people stay heavy or thin people stay thin is due to the story they're telling. Thin people believe they have a fast metabolism, for instance. Heavy people might believe they inherited a tendency to be large. Either way, it's the story we tell. When we say, "No matter what I do, I can't lose weight," that's exactly what we create. When we believe gluten and sugar make us fat, that's exactly what happens when we eat gluten and sugar. The trick is to either work with your beliefs or create new ones. If you believe exercise is the key for you to release pounds because once you start exercising, you get inspired to eat healthier and that's what worked for you in the past, then do that again. If you believe it, you will manifest it.

STEP 4
Meditate

When you meditate and practice alignment, you get in the flow and you can hear your guidance. Meditation is a very individual thing, so you have to find what works for you. When I started releasing pounds, I was doing yoga three to four times a week. I would also go to the gym and listen to Abraham while on the treadmill. This was my way of meditating, and I listened to Abraham repeatedly. As you evolve, you may find yourself incorporating new meditation techniques because what works at one time may not feel so effective later on. But be sure not to skip this step, and why would you even want to? Meditation offers direct access to your Inner Being, who knows how to make life so much easier for you.

STEP 5
Be Flexible

We are constantly evolving, and change is inevitable. It's important to be open to new inspiration, as mentioned above regarding meditation. You may be guided to become a vegetarian one day after years of eating chicken and steak. If it feels good and you're excited about it, that's a sure sign you're on the right track. The important thing is to be happy where you are and eager for more. As you practice being happy, you will receive more clarity. You may find yourself eating a certain way, and then another idea will come along that you find better suited to you at the time. Flexibility will make this process both fun and effective.

Tracy's Story
Guilt Is a Useless Emotion

Guilt creates an incredible amount of confusion and can completely sabotage a person's sincere intent to release pounds for health purposes.

There was a time when food was a reward Tracy allowed herself only after a six-mile run. Fears of gaining weight plagued her mind, while exercise and food deprivation were the only things that eased it. She spent her teenage years through her late 30s depriving herself of food, obsessing over endless workouts and constantly trying to lose weight. When she turned 40, she finally said, "Enough is enough."

Tracy began to make peace with herself and her body although she still wanted to lose 35 pounds. "But maybe I should be happy the way I am," she pondered. "I'm exhausted from starving myself and working out like a crazy person. Maybe it's time I accept myself."

Not long after this revelation, Tracy discovered Abraham-Hicks. She fell in love with the teachings and appreciated how they supported her recent epiphany about self-acceptance. At one time, meditation and visualization were a part of her life, and she began to practice them again. Soon Tracy was inspired to begin a new nutritional program. At first, she was worried that incorporating changes into her existing routine might trigger past obsessions with food and exercise, but things felt different this time. She didn't experience the same anxiety she used to feel whenever she thought about changing her diet. She had studied Abraham enough to know she was now following her Inner Guidance. She was allowing what she wanted to come to her instead of trying to force things to happen.

This inspiration to incorporate a new nutrition program into her life was just that—an inspiration. She felt her Inner Being guiding her and giving clues about what steps to take next, as if these clues were road signs prompting her to turn here or stop there. This program felt good to her with minimal fear involved, unlike in the past. She trusted the guidance and took action. *Inspired action.*

Mindset became one of Tracy's favorite words as she felt her own mind morph into something empowered and confident. Her self-doubt gradually subsided as she meditated and visualized the life and body she desired. Kindness and compassion replaced critical self-talk as her fears transitioned into mere memories that no longer controlled her life.

The new nutritional products agreed with Tracy's body. Her vitality shot through the roof, and she didn't care whether it was due to what she was eating or what she was thinking because the results were extraordinary. After years of depriving herself of the fuel her body needed to function at full throttle, she was thrilled to feel energetic again. Tracy lost 35 pounds within four months and has kept them off for 10 years. That was almost a side benefit due to the energy she felt and how exuberant she became about life. She wanted to shout her experience from the rooftops and let everyone know:

"Give up your worries and your control. Connect with your Inner Being and follow the clues that are there to help you live your absolute best life.

Close your eyes and sit in the silence. Picture what it is you want and feel the feelings as if what you want is happening right now. Do these simple things, and you will no longer feel the need to control everything with your worries and your actions. You can't control any of it anyway. Connect with your Inner Being, allow what you want to come to you and watch your life transform right before your very eyes."

Tracy began to accumulate knowledge about nutrition and fitness. Friends and family were constantly asking her how to lose weight or how to feel better. It became clear the next step for her was to become a Fitness and Mindset Coach. She could feel the guidance coming through, and she was ready.

Her coaching would be different. There would be no diets. There would be no food deprivation, and there would be no counting calories. This would be Law of Attraction-based coaching. In most cases, Tracy found the first step was helping people transition out of the diet mentality that pervades our culture since most people have been on and off diets for years by the time they come to her. "There is a weaning-off period where clients begin to take on new beliefs about the Law of Attraction that replace old beliefs about food deprivation," she explains.

One of Tracy's biggest challenges is getting people to eat. She works with a lot of women who want to release over 100 pounds, and they are afraid to eat the amount of food Tracy recommends. "I personally eat more now than I did 10 years ago, and I'm a size six," says Tracy. "Your body wants and needs nutrition. Getting people to understand this and actually give their bodies enough food is the most difficult part of my coaching process."

"I personally don't deprive myself like I used to," Tracy continues. "If I find myself wanting a donut (I love donuts, by the way), I eat a donut. I don't have guilt about the donut anymore. Abraham talks about how it's a wonder we can find anything to eat because no matter what food we choose, there's some expert somewhere who says it's bad for us."

Helping her clients navigate and eventually dissipate the guilt they experience in regard to food is a big part of Tracy's coaching. "Guilt is a byproduct of the diet mentality that women, especially, learn at a very young age," she points out. "To feel guilty over something you have to do every day (eat) is a real disservice to your body. Guilt creates an incredible amount of confusion and can completely sabotage a person's sincere intent to release pounds for health purposes. I help people work through those feelings of guilt."

Tracy talks about how guilt is simply the result of thoughts you've repeated to yourself over and over for a period of time. Replacing those guilt-ridden thoughts with more productive thoughts about food creates the space for you to begin to trust your body again.

"My philosophy is basically this," continues Tracy, now 54. "If you're going to eat something, enjoy it. It's your alignment and your vibration that matter most. If you're forcing yourself to eat something healthy that you find no satisfaction from whatsoever, don't bother. You're not doing yourself any favors. Manage your alignment and vibration, and eat foods you enjoy. If you really want a donut, have the donut—and enjoy the heck out of it!"

Tracy's 5 Steps

STEP 1
Meditation

Start each day with 15 minutes of meditation. Set a timer and sit with soft music, white noise or whatever brings you into a place of stillness. You can also start with your focus on your breath if that is comfortable for you. The key is to feel good while checking in with your Inner Being. Don't stress it or push the process. You may find that during 14 of the 15 minutes, your mind is wandering or racing around, and you only get that peaceful quiet in the final one minute. That is okay! Meditating shows you where your vibration is, and it's a method by which you can set your point of attraction for the day. I've even stopped in the middle of my day to meditate, especially if I didn't start my day with it. It gives me a reset, and I have found that it makes a positive impact on how the rest of my day will go.

STEP 2
Daily Writing

Some people keep a Book of Positive Aspects where they write all the great things that happened to them during the day. A good appreciation rampage can go in here also. I use my daily writing practice to record how I want to feel and to tell my story the way I want it to be. This writing can be done after you meditate so you can capture and modify those points of attraction that came up for you. For instance, maybe during meditation you started to worry about your ability to attract the body you want, or you started to have some negative self-talk about what you ate last night. Write out exactly *what you want* as if it's happening right now. Write about how you would feel looking in the mirror, seeing your body the way you want it to look. Feel the feelings. Feel the joy as you write. This is extremely powerful.

STEP 3
Visualization
A great deal of visualization can, and probably will, spontaneously happen during your writing process. This can also be done after meditating or when you find yourself slipping in vibration during the day. For some, visualizing images can trigger resistance, so visualizing through feelings can be helpful. Instead of visualizing a phone call with a friend or relative and being triggered to believe there will be some discomfort or resistance, visualize how good it will feel to connect and share positive feelings with that person. Or visualize how you want to feel while walking on the beach or skiing down a mountain. Take those feelings and run with them! You will be surprised by how much your interactions and experiences will positively shift when you focus on the feelings instead of the actions or outcomes.

STEP 4
Create a New Story
To understand the stories you're creating, listen to what you say to yourself and others. Here's a clue: anything that sounds like a complaint is probably not something you want to keep attracting into your life. For instance, if you keep complaining to your girlfriends about how fat you feel or how you keep eating things you shouldn't, that's the story you are recreating each time you tell it. Why not create a new story? The only criterion for creating a new story is that it feels good when you tell it. If you're not ready to tell a new story yet, that's fine. You can still do something. You can stop telling the old story! In

the meanwhile, practice the above steps until your new story begins to emerge.

STEP 5
Be Open to Receive

We don't always know how our good is going to come to us. It often gets delivered in surprising and unexpected ways. Learn to listen to your Inner Guidance. When something is presented to you, ask yourself, "How does this feel?" Practice checking in with your Inner Being. See what feels right to you or what is making you curious to know more. Be open to the path that comes. And if you miss it this time, have no fear. As Abraham says, there are no mistakes. More opportunities will keep coming to you. That's the way it works.

Kristi's Story
Celebrate Your Goddess Body

*Every day, I spend a few minutes writing about how
my body looks and feels as if I've already
attained the body I want.*

Kristi, 34, who now lives in Las Vegas, was raised in New Mexico and Utah with her mom, stepdad, two sisters and brother. It was a difficult childhood with lots of trauma. "I was sexually abused by my stepdad," she says tearfully. "I think that's why I always felt disconnected from my body and why I developed an unhealthy relationship with food. Plus my family was on food stamps, and we were always eating cheap, processed foods, which caused me to gain more weight. At least, that's what I believed for years. Today, I look at things differently."

"Chunky Buns" and "Coconut" were the nicknames Kristi gave herself when she was in elementary school. "It was a way to make fun of myself before anybody else could," she says. Her classmates teased her about her weight when she was young, but she laughed it off. "It wasn't a secret that I was fat. Everybody in my family was big. What hurt me more was that I always felt like an outsider."

Kristi reached her highest weight of 272 pounds after a bad breakup at age 32. "I was only 5'2", so I was pretty big. I was well into a size 20-22 clothing. This was an emotional time in my life. I was very depressed, which led to food binges, which led to more depression and round-and-round it went. After a while, I knew I had to do something. In the past, I had tried all kinds of diets including prescription diet pills. I had dropped 20 pounds taking the pills but stopped because they made me feel jittery. Within three weeks, I gained back the 20 pounds plus some. This time around, after the breakup, I wanted to do something different. Something kept telling me to try yoga, so I finally went to a class."

Yoga turned out to be extremely beneficial for Kristi. The breathing, stretching and movement helped her feel connected to her body for the first time in her adult life. The yoga sessions awakened a desire to explore other tools and philosophies that could open her up even more to feeling better about herself.

Soon she found herself listening to positive, self-help and spiritual videos, eventually discovering an Abraham-Hicks video online. "Something about the message caught my attention, so I kept listening," Kristi recalls. "I really resonated with Abraham. I kept listening whenever I had a free moment. I also loved the stories about Esther and how she applied the Law of Attraction to different situations in her life."

After about a year of listening to Abraham-Hicks and doing yoga, Kristi's self-esteem had increased. Taking her cues from Abraham, she knew the next step for her spiritual growth was meditation. When Kristi started incorporating meditation into her daily routine, her life really began to change. "Meditation gave me something I never experienced before: a calmness and a confidence that is hard to explain," she recounts. "I no longer needed the approval of others. I had a happiness about me that was coming from within, instead of based on circumstances. The things that used to bother me about co-workers and family situations lost some of their charge. I began to love my body 'as is' while thinking about the changes I wanted to make. And I started to lose weight without any real effort on my part. Abraham says that getting happy and in alignment is the secret to everything, and meditation made it even easier for me to get happy. Of course, you can't be happy 24/7, but you get back into alignment as soon as you can. Today I'm one of the happiest people I know, and I love that about myself," Kristi declares.

Once Kristi began meditating, the weight started falling off. In less than a year, she released 62 pounds and went down four sizes. Kristi says the only things she did differently was meditate, get happy, drink lots of water and do yoga. "I didn't go on a diet. I didn't try to cut back on what I ate. I just got happy. It's as simple as that!"

Recently Kristi has been feeling the nudge to eat differently. "Like I said, I didn't try to change my eating. I focused on feeling good emotionally. Lately, however, I feel guided to become a vegetarian. I find myself drawn to healthier foods. This is new. But I didn't lose weight trying to eat less or eat differently. I'm sure I was eating less because I was happier. I ate less because I wasn't depressed. I ate less because I felt better about myself. I ate less because I didn't hate myself anymore. Plus a lot of the stress and fear that used to dominate my existence dissipated since I started meditating. I meditate every morning for 15 minutes before I leave for work. It's like brushing my teeth now."

Kristi has other practices that help her stay in alignment as well as help her attract her desired physical self, including journaling about her "Goddess body." She explains: "Every day, I spend a few minutes writing about how my body looks and feels as if I've already attained the body I want. I write things like, 'I love how curvy and beautiful my body is. I love the shape of my hips and thighs. I am such a magnificent, beautiful Goddess, and I attract positive attention wherever I go. My skin is soft and glowing. My youthfulness exudes a sense of health and vitality. The brightness of my eyes energizes those I connect with. I enjoy buying beautiful and fun clothes for my Goddess body. I am constantly receiving compliments about how attractive I am. While I don't need these compliments, they affirm how I feel about myself. I love the shape of my shoulders and breasts, as well as my waist that curves out where my hips begin. I so love living in this amazing body that enables me to taste food, experience physical pleasure, view beautiful people, nature and art. I am learning how to love myself more and more each day." Kristi believes learning how to transform your body is all about self-love. "Get happy and love yourself. This is the key to everything."

Kristi's 5 Steps

STEP 1
Get Happy

Find out what makes you happy and do more of that. In fact, make your happiness your number one priority. Fill your mind with positive teachings. Listen to and read Abraham-Hicks. Make lists of Positive Aspects about your life. Ask yourself throughout your day, "What would make me feel better right now? What would make me happier?"

STEP 2
Meditate

Meditation can change your life. I meditate for about 30 minutes a day, usually 15 minutes in the morning before I leave for work and 15 minutes before I go to sleep. I will often listen to a meditation with a binaural beat in the background at bedtime, which increases relaxation and has many other benefits. I also attend meditation circles and use various meditation apps for guided meditations. I am a much happier person when I meditate.

STEP 3
Practice Self-Love and Self-Care

I often write quotes on sticky notes and paste them on the mirrors around my apartment to help remind me to love myself. Other ways I practice self-care include going to yoga and getting massages. Taking time to love yourself is the way you undo all the years of criticizing yourself. What are some ways you can practice self-care? Whether it's a walk in nature, a mani-pedi or taking five minutes out of your day to meditate, do what works for you and build on that.

STEP 4
Journal

I love to journal. I journal about what I want as if it's already happened. I journal about my body as if I've already attained the body I desire. I journal about my abundance as if I've already attained the level of prosperity I want. I journal about my relationships as if I'm already in the relationship I dream about. I journal about where I live as if I'm already in the house I see in my mind. And when I journal about these things, I feel the emotions as if they are happening right now. As a result, my life keeps improving!

STEP 5
Visualize

Visualization is a lot like journaling, except you're not writing about it. You are closing your eyes and imagining those things you want and feeling the feelings as if they are happening right now. It is equally effective as journaling, and that's why I do both.

Debbie's Story
You Get What You Expect

I believe you get what you expect. I've lost 108 pounds because I lined up with what I wanted—and expected it.

D ebbie's story demonstrates the power of expectation. You can apply her message to *any* area of your life, including learning how to love (or love *and* transform) your body. "Whatever I do and whatever is going on in my world, I believe I get exactly what I expect," says Debbie, age 61.

Debbie had reached 300 pounds and was diagnosed with diabetes. That was her wake-up call. "My doctor put me on a diabetes medication that is commonly known to cause weight loss," she explains. "I decided to use the side effects of the medication to jumpstart my transition to a healthier body." She had been studying Abraham-Hicks for many years and enjoyed great success applying it to other areas of life. Now it was time to apply what she knew about the Law of Attraction to her health. "I was well-versed in the power of beliefs and expectations, so I decided to *expect* to lose one pound a day," she continues. "And that's exactly what happened. Every day I got on the scale, I was one pound lighter.

Before I knew it, I lost 45 pounds and was feeling so much better. My shortness of breath improved as did my energy."

Then something *unexpected* happened. Debbie and her husband lost their health insurance. They found themselves in a dilemma because the diabetes medication cost $250 per month. Debbie checked in with her Inner Being and felt the nudge to go off the medication. She was feeling much better due to releasing the 45 pounds and didn't want to incur the $250 expense each month. Her doctor gave permission.

Persevering with her health journey, Debbie continued her practice of expecting to lose weight. She made up her mind to *expect* to lose the next 40-50 pounds easily and quickly. It was clear to her that manifesting anything in life was about thoughts, feelings and expectations. "The diabetes medication helped to get my weight loss started, and looking back, it was probably my path of least resistance," says Debbie. "It also helped me create momentum toward releasing the rest of the weight."

It took Debbie one year to reach her goal of releasing over 100 pounds (she lost 108 pounds, which averages out to more than two pounds per week), and she's kept it off for three years. Debbie says she didn't diet at all. In fact, she has an aversion to dieting. "It never worked for me," she shares. "What works for me is understanding how the Law of Attraction operates and consciously applying it to my life."

While many women find it counter-productive to weigh themselves, Debbie thrived on it. "When I was on the diabetes medication, I expected to lose a pound a day—and I did. Sometimes I would actually see the number on the scale in my mind first. It was like the scale was responding to the picture in my head." While there was no diabetes medicine involved in the last 63 pounds Debbie released, there was a lot of expectation. "I built up so much momentum in believing I would lose the weight that it continued happening," she says.

Debbie is now off all medications, including blood pressure medicine. People often ask how she lost the weight and got healthy. She is pretty tight-lipped about it because she realizes how far-fetched it sounds to those who don't understand the Law of Attraction. "If I tell them the truth, that I simply expected to lose the weight, that I didn't exercise or change the way I eat, most of them will think I've lost my mind, so I really don't share much about it. It is most likely metabolically impossible for me to have eaten what I ate and still lose weight, but that's exactly what happened. I know it's my beliefs and my expectation that created the results," Debbie asserts. "Did I lean a little more in the direction of healthy eating? I guess so, but I wouldn't say I've been on a diet. I've eaten ice cream in the midst of all this. Is it possible that if someone analyzed what I ate, they would find that I ate significantly fewer calories than I used to eat? Maybe. But I doubt it. That's not how it occurred to me. I believe you get what you expect, and that's how I manifested this weight loss. I've lost 108 pounds because I lined up with what I wanted—and totally expected it."

About 17 years ago, Debbie did in fact go on a restrictive diet and got down to 180 pounds but quickly gained it back. "I lost my motivation to keep eating carrots, celery and romaine lettuce because that was all I was allowed to eat. I couldn't live that way, so I gave up. I decided if people didn't like me the way I am, the heck with them," she recalls. There were a lot of people who were critical of Debbie's size, and many friends, family members and work associates had tried to get her to lose weight. "I never responded well to others telling me what to do," she clarifies. "I think that's how I ended up with an aversion to doing anything about my weight. Not that I'm blaming my health challenges on anyone else. I know I'm responsible for my own reality, and I know many of these individuals were trying to help because they loved me. It's just that I believe the inspiration to transform has to come from within and not from outside pressure."

Debbie didn't know about the Law of Attraction until the movie *The Secret* came out in 2006. She learned about it when she landed two tickets to *The Oprah Winfrey Show* that featured some of the experts from the movie. "There were two or three back-to-back programs about *The Secret* on *The Oprah Winfrey Show*, and I was in the audience for two of them. You were only allowed to go to one taping per year, but somehow I got to go to both of those shows. Life changed for me after seeing those episodes because I began to understand how things really work. I began to understand that it is my mind that creates my reality. My mind was creating my reality all along, but now I was aware of it." Once she saw *The Secret*, Debbie began repeatedly hearing about Abraham. She sought out this Abraham and read *Ask and It Is Given*. It resonated well with her, and every page was more eye-opening than the last.

Awareness of the Law of Attraction helps Debbie manifest more than weight loss. She frequently enters contests and often wins free trips. She recently manifested a free trip to Hawaii with her husband. She has also manifested many lucrative financial opportunities and a life she loves in Chicago with her family and beloved pets.

"Life is a thousand times more fun since applying the Law of Attraction to my health," says Debbie. "When I was 100 pounds heavier, I barely left the couch when I was home. Moving from one room to the other was a challenge. Everything hurt. Now I'm up and down the stairs all day. I take walks in the woods. It's all about expectation. I expected these things to happen and they did."

Debbie's 5 Steps

STEP 1
You Get What You Expect

Expectation is about belief. If you want to lose weight but you believe you can't, then you won't. It's that simple. You've got to find a way to expect it to happen. You must find a way to believe that it will happen. You always get what you expect.

STEP 2
Seek Alignment

Alignment is the fundamental teaching of Abraham-Hicks. If you want something to happen but you really don't believe it will, most likely you are out of alignment. It is difficult to feel emotionally good (be in alignment) when you want something but believe you can't have it. If you can get yourself to feel better about your ability to manifest it, you can make your way to belief and expectation. So yes, they are tied together.

STEP 3
Trust Yourself

Stop listening to what everybody else is telling you to do unless what they are saying resonates with you. People may be well-meaning, but we each have our own Inner Guidance. Someone else can't possibly know what is best for you. Start listening and trusting yourself.

STEP 4
Watch What You Feed Your Brain

Since I've discovered the Law of Attraction, I'm very picky about what I read, watch and discuss. You can't shield yourself from all the bad news, but you can make many choices about what kind of information you're exposed to. Choose wisely.

STEP 5
Keep Expanding

Keep expanding, keep growing and keep learning. Since you get what you expect, it's important to do whatever you need to do to support the belief that you create your reality with your mind. Hang out with like-minded people who will cheer you on. Grow spiritually. This is the way you nourish your dreams.

Ramona's Story
Life After Love

I'm focusing on what feels good and not how much I weigh. I'm feeling strong and healthy and I love it!

Five years ago when Ramona was 55, her partner of 23 years was dying. Ramona knew it was coming and yet when it happened, she was devastated. Betty died of pancreatic cancer eight months after she was diagnosed. Ramona had no intentions of living without Betty because, at the time, she believed Betty was her only source of unconditional love. When the nurse from hospice asked for the left-over morphine, Ramona neglected to tell her about the small vial hidden away in a drawer. Later that night, Ramona composed the suicide note she planned to leave one week later after her affairs were in order.

The next day, Ramona received a phone call from Betty's best friend, Lina. Ramona remembered how calm Lina had been when the love of her life died years ago. Lina's husband went in for a simple out-patient procedure on his hand. When they came home that night, he said his legs were hurting, so Lina rubbed them before going to the restroom. When she returned, he was dead.

Now it was Ramona who had lost her loved one, and Lina comforted Ramona for over an hour. Feeling a tiny spark of hope, Ramona asked, "How did you do it, Lina? You were so calm when Harry died. And I know how much you loved him. I don't understand."

That's when Lina told Ramona about Abraham-Hicks. "It's not that I didn't grieve," said Lina. "But I had been studying Abraham-Hicks for many years, and I knew there really is no such thing as death. I knew I wasn't losing Harry. I could still talk to him. I could still feel his presence. Plus, I had tools I learned from Abraham...ways to handle my grief. I had choices. I didn't have to be miserable."

The next day, Ramona went to the library to check out the Abraham-Hicks books Lina recommended, *Ask and It Is Given* and *The Vortex*. These books, and other Abraham audio materials she listened to over the next few months, helped Ramona decide she wanted to go on living. She even heard Esther Hicks talk about the transition of her husband, Jerry, into non-physical. "Esther Hicks and Lina saved my life," says Ramona. (Esther and Jerry Hicks are the authors of the Abraham-Hicks books). "Through their example, I discovered I could get through the pain of losing Betty."

Ramona learned about the importance of alignment (deliberately choosing to feel good emotionally) by studying Abraham. "In the beginning, it was like ping pong," she recalls. "I was in and out of alignment so much my head hurt. Gradually I experienced more consistency. And then one day it dawned on me that if I could use the Law of Attraction to help me handle Betty's transition, maybe I could use it for other things like getting back to my desired weight."

Ramona was always slim until she reached her late thirties. When she started to gain weight, she began going to doctors to learn why. Eventually she was diagnosed with Hashimoto's thyroiditis which, they said, caused her weight gain. "I started going to the gym and doing everything I was supposed to do—but nothing worked," recounts Ramona. "I kept gaining through my 50s, ultimately reaching 220 pounds. I tried it all, including every kind of diet out there. I even went on the HCG diet where they inject you with a pregnancy hormone and you basically starve yourself. I lost 40 pounds, but as soon as my partner transitioned, I gained it all back."

Discovering Abraham gave her new inspiration, and practicing alignment and meditation led to a feeling of hope. Ramona soon felt the impulse to put out an intention to the Universe that she was open to a different way of eating that felt good (where she wasn't always hungry). She also became very intentional about loving her body in its current state. Soon after setting those intentions, Ramona went on an Abraham-Hicks cruise to the Greek Islands. On that cruise, she made some new friends. "I noticed they were very healthy-looking. They eventually shared their eating style with me, and I could feel my Inner Being saying, 'Yes, yes, yes!' I knew immediately what they were talking about resonated with me and fit with my beliefs. I went home and adopted this way of eating, and the weight just fell off. I went from 220 to 180."

Ramona says she would like to lose another 30 pounds, but she's not worried about it. The most important thing to her is her alignment. She also says she never talks about losing weight. Instead she talks about gaining leanness. She knows how she wants to fit in her clothes and feel in her body. "I am focusing on what feels good and not how much I weigh," she adds. "I'm feeling strong and healthy, and I love it!"

Ramona's 5 Steps

STEP 1
Get in Alignment
Make alignment your number one priority. I have multiple tools I use on a regular basis to help me get into alignment. I choose the tool based on my current state of mind.

Here are some examples of the specific tool I might use for different moods:

- Tired or stressed: Take a long, hot bath or a nap.
- Anxious: Watch funny videos, do a puzzle, play a game.
- Hungry in between meals: Have a snack with some water.
- Mind racing: Meditate.
- Bored: Physical activity such as kayaking/hiking/working out.
- Lonely: Phone a high-vibing friend (someone who is usually in a good mood).
- Neutral to slightly low-vibe (feeling out of sorts): Jumping jacks. They always make me laugh, reminding me of my childhood.

STEP 2
Know Your Beliefs
If you're looking for a food plan to help you release pounds, it's very helpful to know what your beliefs are around the subject. If your beliefs don't line up with your actions, it's most likely not going to work. When I decided to do Keto, that decision felt right to me. It fit in perfectly with my beliefs about food and as a result, I had great success.

STEP 3

Meditate

There are many ways to meditate. For instance, I meditate while I'm doing the dishes or cleaning the house. I also meditate three times per week sitting in a chair or on my bed. Meditation is very important. It's like getting a direct line to your Inner Being. The clarity and peace you gain from meditation puts you in the fast lane of your spiritual growth. It also adjusts your perspective. What you once thought was so important becomes less important when you meditate. You are calmer, happier and more tuned in to the messages from your Inner Being. I've found meditation to be extremely helpful in diminishing my preoccupation with food.

STEP 4

Visualize

If you are kinesthetic like me, using your imagination to create pictures in your mind of how you want your body to look seems like a foreign concept. However, that doesn't mean I haven't found visualization extremely effective in releasing pounds and getting fit. I do what I call "kinesthetic visualization." For instance, I run my hands over my abdomen and imagine it feeling flatter and firmer, the way it used to be. I run my hands down my thighs and imagine feeling the ridges of nice, tight, smooth muscles right below the surface of my skin. Then I sneak in a bit of regular visualization and see myself jumping and running, sprinting and climbing trees, doing all kinds of cool stuff with these really strong legs.

STEP 5
Identify Your Intention

It's important to get clear about your intentions. Once you zero in on an intention, such as "I want to get in shape," or "I want to allow my perfect health to appear," then it's time to let go and listen. Go about your business while being aware of the messages you are receiving. Remain open-eared, open-eyed and open-minded to the little nudges from the Universe guiding you to your next steps. In other words, pay attention. Look for the signs. You are being guided every step of the way toward your wants and desires, but you've got to be awake enough to notice.

Susan's Story
Fun Is My Medicine

Every time I have fun, something good happens.

In 2009, Susan, 40, who lives in Trinidad, gave birth to her second child via C-section. While her son was healthy, Susan wasn't. After the birth, doctors discovered many of Susan's organs were in jeopardy, and they couldn't determine the reason. After a dozen tests and no definitive answers, they handed her a paper containing a regimented diet and sent her home.

Susan sought the help of a nutritionist, who reinforced the importance of following the strict diet. "In the beginning I was terrified, so I tried my best to follow the food plan, but I couldn't do it," shares Susan. "There were too many rules and nothing on the list that I enjoyed eating. I felt terrible about myself because this was a life-and-death situation. At least, that's the way the doctors described it to me."

Soon afterward, Susan started listening to Abraham-Hicks and decided to try a different approach. "Abraham talks about weight, money, love, health and more...all these lovely things. I didn't understand the Law of Attraction (how we attract what we want into our lives through our thoughts and feelings) until I started listening to

Abraham. I learned that life is easier when you get quiet, meditate and tune in to your Inner Being. Abraham also talks about being inspired to eat healthier—that it's not something you have to force. I learned that I can influence my health with my thoughts, and that the most important thing is to focus on my emotions and how I can feel happier by adjusting those thoughts," says Susan.

After listening to Abraham, Susan realized how stressed she had been prior to getting sick. "I used to work for a Caribbean cruise line, so I had a really exciting job and made a lot of friends. I loved it. When I came back to Trinidad, there was something missing. I had my family and a beautiful life, but I missed my job. And then both my parents got ill, bringing much stress, negativity and drama. I didn't know how to handle it all or how to cope. I think it was the stress that caused my health problems. When I started listening to Abraham-Hicks, everything changed."

"I started eating healthier and losing weight, and it wasn't a struggle," Susan continues. "It seemed to happen naturally. Within one year, I lost 30 pounds and never dieted. Instead, I focused on my happiness, and the happier I felt, the more I started to crave healthier foods. I wanted more greens. I wanted more fruits and vegetables. Then one day I realized that I was literally healing my organs and repairing my cells— not only through what I was eating but also through what I was thinking and feeling. I listened to Abraham as much as I could and found that I began to love myself more and more."

Today Susan is off all former medications. Her cholesterol, which was extremely high when she was sick, is now normal. When people ask her how she lost 30 pounds, she tells them she decided to be happy and have fun with what she eats and with life in general. "Just have fun," says Susan. "In fact, my favorite saying is 'Every time I have fun, something good happens.' And it's true. Whenever I'm having fun, I win something or get some extra money. It all works out." Susan admits there could still be drama that could cause stress in her life—if she let it. But she is determined to make alignment her number one priority. "The more I focus on the good, the more I am calm no matter what is going on around me."

Susan finds it amazing how the Law of Attraction works. She often talks about the many "coincidences" that bring things to her she didn't even know she wanted or needed. One example is a resource for natural spring water she stumbled upon "accidentally" one day. "I started drinking spring water after I got sick," she says. "It's all I drink. One day, I found a free natural resource for unlimited spring water two hours from my house. Once a month, I drive there in my pick-up and fill my containers with the water. My family also drinks it, and I cook with it. I believe this water has contributed to my health and healing."

Self-love is a big part of Susan's transformation as well. "Even though I'm not skinny, I no longer criticize myself about it," she shares. "I love myself. I love how I feel. Even the way I breathe is different, and everything just flows nicely. I attract healthy foods, healthy people and a lot of things I ask for just come to me. I asked to be healed. I asked to be whole. I asked to be healthy. At first, I hardly knew where to start, but in the process of asking, the answers and resources eventually came."

This way of life has spilled over to Susan's children, ages 14 and 11 who, like Susan, now meditate almost every day. "They're doing exceptionally well in school," she confides with pride. "Their report cards are flawless. I never had a problem with them in that area. The meditation works for them because it gives them a sense of independence. Their teachers also tell me my kids are confident. I think the meditation is the reason for this calmness and confidence. They trust themselves. They listen to their own Inner Guidance. They also listen to the Abraham recordings. It's difficult for them not to, since I play the recordings almost every day while I'm cooking!"

Susan is excited about her future. Currently she is a Family Life Counselor, sharing everything she's learned with as many families in her community as she can. She is also a PhD candidate at OASIS University Trinidad.

Susan's 5 Steps

STEP 1
Pay Attention to Your Feelings

I'm usually a happy person, but I previously let stress get the best of me. Now I don't allow things to get that far. I meditate, listen to Abraham and do whatever else it takes to make sure I'm feeling good. We are so lucky to know this secret to life. I wish I could share it with everyone.

STEP 2
Love Yourself

I didn't always love myself. I put everybody else ahead of me. I thought I was fat and that made me ugly. Feeling happy is not possible if you are always criticizing yourself. When I learned to love myself, I started to take better care of my body. I started to eat healthier foods. I started to dress nicer and say nicer things to myself. Life is so much more fun when you love yourself!

STEP 3
Meditate

Meditation helps you minimize toxic thoughts. Without these toxic thoughts running your life and creating all kinds of unnecessary stress and drama, you are able to understand yourself and others more readily. Meditation also helps you tap in to your Inner Guidance. When you are tuned in to this guidance, you feel calmer, happier and more confident. There are so many benefits to meditating that it's silly not to do it. My eating got better when I meditated and so did my health. Abraham recommends meditating, and that's reason enough for me to do it. It has changed my life.

STEP 4
Visualize

I taped a photo of myself when I was 21 and at my ideal weight to the inside of my cupboard so I would see it every day. I also wrote and pasted affirmations in my bathroom and in the cupboard next to my photo. These affirmations remind me of who I am. I also bought clothes for a trip to England that I am planning but haven't booked yet. I look at these clothes every day, and they help me visualize my trip. Visualization is very powerful, and there are many ways to do it. You can find what works for you.

STEP 5
Have Fun

Every time I have fun, something good happens. That's my motto in life. Ask yourself throughout your day, "Am I having fun?" If not, change what you're doing, and if you can't change what you're doing, change how you're thinking about what you're doing. Abraham is always talking about our vibration. Fun is a super-high vibration, and when you are vibrating at this frequency, you allow the things you want to come into your life. So have some fun!

Rose's Story
Does It Spark Joy?

Whatever eating style you choose, ask yourself,
does it feel good to me? Does it spark joy?
If the answer is no, try something else.

The women in Rose's family in Texas were all tiny. Rose was also petite but found herself feeling self-conscious when she started gaining weight in elementary school. "Looking back, that's when I started eating unconsciously. I think I overate to soothe myself because I felt lonely. I would come home from school and eat an entire bag of chips drowned in hot sauce."

When Rose started high school, she joined the majorettes. "We wore cute little outfits with cowboy boots, and I wanted to look like the other girls. That's when the dieting started. I would freeze diet drinks (liquid meal replacements) and drink one before practice. That's how I stayed thin throughout high school," she recalls.

"During my first marriage (there were three of them), I gained over 30 pounds," says Rose. "When I decided I wanted to return to my smaller size, I joined a popular weight-loss program and got back down to 123 pounds. Throughout my adult life, well into my early sixties, my weight fluctuated between the 120s and mid-160s. The lighter weight made me eager to move. I loved to walk, dance and hike, but when I gained extra weight, I lost some interest in those activities."

"My third and most recent husband, who I thought I would spend the rest of my life with, asked me for a divorce after 11 years of marriage," Rose reveals. "Suddenly I was faced with the premise of starting over at 65. Only days before his unexpected departure, I had been planning our retirement. These plans were now replaced with finding a new job, a new apartment and a new life."

"Instead of feeling sorry for myself, I was deeply thankful for the teachings of Abraham-Hicks," she continues. "When I went through that last divorce and got a job (instead of a retirement plan with my husband), I learned to make it 'the best thing that ever happened to me.' And it is. I have so much fun at work. I am deeply appreciated there and meet countless wonderful people. I have the freedom to make my own decisions and interestingly enough, I feel that I'm getting younger!"

During her third divorce, Rose wanted to lose the same 40 pounds that seemed to keep reappearing. But this time, she wanted to keep it off. Her new philosophy, influenced by Abraham, was weight loss could be fun, easy and fast. She checked in with her Inner Being and felt a strong urge to go back on the program that worked so well previously. "It was the path of least resistance for me," says Rose. "Abraham talks about easy and fun, and this is what felt good."

Rose did not feel deprived when she was on this program. "I've heard people say dieting leads to bingeing, but this did not feel like dieting. How could it? I eat whatever I want. I so appreciate what Abraham says about 'how we feel' is more important than 'what we eat.' The eating style you choose should spark joy in you, as Marie Kondo, author of *The Life-Changing Magic of Tidying Up*, would say. Since joy is unique to each individual, there is no correct way to eat. You name any food nutritional experts say to avoid, and I guarantee you somebody has thrived for a hundred years eating it!"

"I saw a documentary that portrayed humans as the only creatures to gain weight except for bears and domestic critters fed by us humans," continues Rose. "All other species know and live the clarity of natural fitness and thriving. The less we analyze what we should and shouldn't eat and the more we savor food and life, the more we allow that thriving. So whatever eating style you choose, make sure it's easy and fun. If it's hard work, forget it. If you're stressing out, try something else. It's all about your alignment and vibration, meaning your decision to focus in good-feeling ways. Tell your Inner Being you want to lose weight (or whatever it is you want). Relax, ask for guidance and wait. The solution may not come immediately, but it will come. When you put your alignment first, when you practice connecting with your Inner Being, it's impossible not to receive guidance."

Rose makes it a point to notice what makes her feel good. "It feels good to me to be able to fit into my clothes. It also feels good to be aware of what I'm eating. When I go unconscious with my food, I'm not really tasting it and enjoying it, so I eat more." It also feels good to Rose to love herself. "I adore myself. That wasn't always the case, but today it is. I think I'm precious. When I look at myself in the mirror and think of how much there is to love instead of focusing on the imperfections, I feel great."

Rose has re-invented her entire life in the past three years. "Along with my marital status, I've changed my wardrobe plus everything in my house and cupboards. I've gotten rid of all that doesn't spark joy. I choose to appreciate and adore my life, including myself. I feel like the past three years have been gifted to me—setup by Source so I could transform. I've lost 35 of the 40 pounds I've wanted to lose, and I've kept them off for over a year. It has been fun, easy and fast. There were occasional days where my alignment was off and I went back to unconscious eating, but I didn't freak out about it. I was easy on myself instead."

"Life is full of contrast—experiences you want and those you don't want," Rose continues. "When you're upset, you can choose to focus in new ways and feel better. You're either feeling emotionally good or not. You're either in alignment or not. The point is to keep getting better at feeling good."

Rose recently returned to one of her great loves, hiking. "I now go on 10-mile hikes in the beautiful mountains of North Carolina with a hiking group of fabulous folks of all ages. I started out with three-mile hikes last year and worked my way up to 10. My blood pressure medicine has been reduced, and my few aches and pains are a distant memory. My endorphins, 'inner dolphins' as I call them, are regularly released, and I appreciate my well-being as eternally natural. On the verge of my 69th birthday, I feel better than I did years ago! My hiking hobby fell into place when I became clear that I am an active elder. I adore being alive and surrounding myself on all levels with what sparks joy."

Rose's 5 Steps

STEP 1
Practice Alignment
Be in alignment when eating. (Be in alignment when doing anything!) Food tastes better when you're relaxed and happy, and your body benefits more. Your metabolism will work more efficiently and so will everything else.

STEP 2
Focus on What You Want
Here's a tip to know whether you're focusing on what you want: Ask yourself, "How do I feel right now?" If you feel good (in the vicinity of happy, peaceful, hopeful or content), you are focusing on what you want. If you don't feel good, you are focusing on something you don't want. It sounds simple and it is simple. Focusing on what you want with feel-good emotions is how you attract your desires.

STEP 3
Appreciate Your Body and Your Food
Appreciate the heck out of your body and the heck out of your food! In fact, appreciate the heck out of everything, even life's contrast that sometimes throws you for a loop. Reframe things so they feel better. Whatever is happening, try to make it the best ever. Since I've been following Abraham-Hicks, the food is the best I've ever tasted. I'm adoring it all. I also love and appreciate my body more than I have in my entire life. I'm seeing it all through the eyes of Source, and there's a wonderful lightness to that approach. The more you appreciate, the more you will have to appreciate.

STEP 4
Work with Your Beliefs

It is important to work with your beliefs as opposed to working against them. Abraham-Hicks calls this the "path of least resistance." For instance, if you believe certain supplements or foods are essential to your well-being, then by all means, stick with those. What you believe to be true *is* true for you. What works for someone else may not necessarily work for you because they hold different beliefs from yours. If you want to lose weight, find out what your beliefs are about weight loss and do that. It's the easiest path!

STEP 5
Ask Yourself, "Does This Spark Joy?"

When I decided I wanted to lose 40 pounds, I knew I had to make it fun or it wasn't going to work. I suggest creating your own little catch-phrase or mantra that helps to remind you this is supposed to be fun. I have two: "Fun, easy and fast!" and "Does this spark joy?" That's the benchmark I use to see if I'm on the right track. Is this fun? Does it spark joy? Am I enjoying my food? Am I enjoying the process? Fun is my number one priority in all things. If I'm having fun, that means I'm in alignment, and when I'm in alignment I attract what I want, including the body and life I desire.

Laura's Story
The Balance Beam

The weight gains always seemed connected to my feelings of unworthiness, followed by a dose of hopelessness about my love life. Thankfully, I discovered Abraham-Hicks.

As a young girl and a competitive gymnast living in Tampa, Florida, Laura, now 44, used to weigh in at the beginning of each gymnastics practice. Her coaches weren't always happy with the results. As she recalls, her weight seemed more important than how many medals she won. It got to the point where Laura felt her self-worth came from the number on the scale. When she hit puberty, it seemed that her body rebelled against the pressure. She began to gain more weight, sending her gymnastics coaches into a frenzy. To control the situation, her coaches assigned her to the treadmill instead of the balance beam whenever she weighed in too high. "Today I know better than to blame others for things I don't like about my life. But at the time, I felt like I was being punished," says Laura. "I felt isolated from my friends and from the sport I loved whenever they put me on the treadmill."

In an attempt to appease her coaches, Laura's mom took her to Jenny Craig®. Laura was 15 years old, and they would not accept her into the program because she didn't have enough body fat. "I wasn't fat enough for Jenny Craig® and I wasn't thin enough for gymnastics," she recalls.

At 16, Laura finally quit. "I got to the point where I wanted to stop the fight, so I did. I quit the team and started binge-eating when my parents were not around. I wanted to have something I could control because I felt so out of control. That's when the yo-yo dieting started. I would get very thin and then gain 40 pounds very quickly."

When Laura was in her early 30s, she lived in Vail, Colorado, where she walked over 12 miles a day at her job in a ski resort. She was able to maintain her ideal weight for nearly four years while there. "Once I got a more sedentary position in my field, I jumped right back onto the yo-yo dieting merry-go-round. The weight gains always seemed connected to my feelings of unworthiness, followed by a dose of hopelessness about my love life. I didn't love myself, and I believed that nobody else would ever love me. Thankfully, I discovered Abraham-Hicks, which transformed my thinking."

The more Laura read and listened to the Abraham-Hicks teachings, the more she began to understand she attracted her own experiences through her thoughts. She found this knowledge extremely liberating. No longer did she blame her gymnastics coaches or her parents for trying to control her weight all those years. "I realized that I created my own reality back then, just like I create my own reality now. By knowing this principle, I can choose to focus on what I want, instead of what I don't want." The new experiences Laura wanted to create included losing those same 40 pounds for good, becoming free from her obsession with her body and no longer basing her self-worth on her weight.

"One day I decided I was going to love my current body—as is. I also decided I wanted to manifest my ideal body. Not a gymnast's body, but a body that feels fit and realistic to me now," Laura shares. "Without expectation or attachment to the outcome, I began to practice visualizing and feeling as if I was at my ideal weight. In addition, I stopped focusing on the 'what is' and avoided mirrors and photos of myself. I kept a vision in my mind of what I wanted to look like and focused on that. I pretended I was already there—at my ideal weight and fitness level. Any time I exercised, (including my 30-minute walks each day), I imagined what it feels like to have tight muscles in my legs and arms. I would not only visualize, I would experience feelings of satisfaction as if I had already manifested these things."

Laura decided she was going to focus on feeling physically strong (as opposed to losing weight) because "strong" was a word that didn't have any resistance for her. Throughout the day, when thoughts about her body popped up, she would remind herself once again that she was strong. It was important to Laura not to focus on this new body in order to attract a lover or a relationship or to please other people. She wanted to do it for herself this time.

Laura did eventually release the 40 pounds, but more important, she enjoys a new attitude about her body. "Before, I felt like I had to change my weight to change my life. Now I've been focusing on accepting and loving myself. I don't feel the need to control my weight so much. I want to have energy. I want to feel a sense of vitality, and I want to look good in my clothes *for me*," she proclaims. "I was very hard on myself in the past. I thought I should have this perfect body that was nearly impossible to maintain. There's a little more give now. Today I'm more comfortable in my own skin. I'm learning how to love myself."

Laura's 5 Steps

STEP 1
Stop Paying Attention to What Is
If you keep focusing on the "what is" (where you are now), you will keep manifesting more of the same. Instead, focus on what you want. Keep your mind on your ideal body. Avoid any evidence that supports what you don't want. At the same time, even though it sounds like a contradiction, you've got to love and accept the "what is." If you're hating yourself at your current weight, you won't be able to think about your ideal body because you're submerged in your hatred. The Universe gives back to you what you focus on. It's that simple.

STEP 2
Visualize
Start feeling what it would be like to have the body you want. Whenever you're in a good mood, start imagining fitting into the clothing size you prefer. Or see yourself at your cousin's wedding looking hot in your new dress. Picture the toned muscles in your legs and arms. Whatever it is for you, start feeling the feelings as if you've just achieved it. What does it feel like to be at that wedding wearing that dress? Act it out in your mind. What does it feel like to see those muscles on your thighs? Pretend you are looking in the mirror and seeing them right now. Feeling the emotions is the key.

STEP 3
Be Nice to Yourself
Forgive yourself. Stop blaming yourself for your inadequacies or for things that are going badly in your life. Learn to have compassion for the struggle you've had in the past. Treat yourself like you would treat a best friend that was having a bad day. If your friend came to you and

said, "I can't find love. I'm too fat," you probably would respond supportively and compassionately. You would probably sincerely tell them that they *will* find someone who's going to love them just the way they are. We need to show ourselves the same kindness.

STEP 4
Let Go of the Illusion
If listening to Abraham has taught me anything, it's that we all want something because we think we will be happier once we get it. "I'll be happy when I get that job." "I'll be happy when I get married." "I'll be happy when I lose weight." Abraham teaches us that the way to manifest what we want is to be happy now. If we are not happy during the journey, chances are we won't be happy when we get there. I have learned to let go of the expectation that losing weight is the key to my happiness. Focus on getting happy now, and you will also be happy when you achieve that goal you want.

STEP 5
Stop Comparing Yourself to Others
Comparing yourself to others is a trap. It stops you from being happy in the moment and from appreciating yourself. So many of us compare ourselves to skinny women and feel unworthy. I did it for years. "Why can't I be thin?" "Why can't I stay thin?" "What's wrong with me?" "I have no willpower." "I'm not desirable because I'm not skinny like them." This kind of thinking prevents you from loving yourself. If you want to have a smaller physique, there's nothing wrong with that, but stop putting yourself down. Loving yourself is a much more productive way of going about it.

Melissa's Story
Nudges from the Universe

It was almost like I downloaded a custom-made list of what to eat for my body directly from Source. I knew exactly what to do, and everything on the food plan aligned with my beliefs.

From November 2017 to April 2018, Melissa, 51, felt as if she was slipping into a giant black hole. Everything that could go wrong, did. Her dad had a stroke, the love of her life left her and she was at her highest weight ever. Melissa felt alone, overwhelmed and hopeless. Something had to change.

That change started with Melissa's commitment to study Abraham-Hicks. A few of the Abraham books collecting dust on her bookshelf were now calling her name. She retrieved the books, dusted them off and started reading. Soon after that, she found herself joining Abraham-Hicks Facebook groups and listening to Abraham videos whenever she had a spare moment.

Once Melissa began to immerse herself in Abraham's teachings, she started to receive what she calls "nudges from the Universe." One such nudge was a clear, detailed picture of a food plan. "It was almost like I downloaded a custom-made list of what to eat for my body directly from Source," says Melissa. "I knew exactly what to do, and everything on the food plan aligned with my beliefs." To Melissa's surprise, her next nudge was to take up running. She was athletic for most of her life but never enjoyed running. Yet there she was, out in the cold Canadian winter, running three times a week after work. Her body was getting stronger and stronger.

Melissa is a firm believer in positive self-talk. She calls it *self-soothing*. "I had gotten into the habit of negative self-talk, and now it was time to reverse that," she explains. "Abraham speaks about the importance of focusing on what you want with your thoughts and your words. Up-leveling my self-talk is a tool I find extremely helpful. For instance, when I was training to do a 10k run, I would sometimes fall back into negative thoughts. I would get discouraged or not feel like training that day. That's when I would make a conscious decision to go into overdrive with positive reinforcement. I would say things to myself like, 'Melissa, look how strong you are. You keep getting more and more fit. You are literally sweating off the pounds you could never get rid of before.'"

When Melissa experienced trepidation around trying new sports, she would say to herself, "You would never have tried this in the past, but you are open to new experiences now. Look how much fun you're having with your friends! Isn't it great being active and adventurous?" This kind of self-cheerleading led to Melissa jumping into all kinds of new adventures including kayaking, mountain biking and Tough Mudders (endurance events where participants attempt 10- to 12-mile-long obstacle courses).

Learning to self-soothe also helped Melissa feel good about her food choices. "In the mornings, I would tell myself, 'This breakfast is feeding my cells. This protein shake provides me with all the nutrients I need to start my day. I deserve an abundance of nutrients.' The more I fed myself positive thoughts, the better I felt."

The positive self-talk also helped her get through the times she ate things she thought she shouldn't. She simply practiced talking herself into feeling good again. "I learned from Abraham that there was no point in beating myself up about food choices," adds Melissa. "However, that's exactly what I used to do. In the past, every time I ate something I believed wasn't good for me, I would criticize myself to no end. I would work myself up into such a frenzy that I might have a mini-panic attack about it. I don't do that anymore. Today if my body wants pizza, I eat pizza and I soothe myself. I tell myself it's okay. It's no big deal. I go right back to loving my body and myself. Changing how I talk to myself has made all the difference in the world."

"The thing is," Melissa continues, "we have been programmed to believe that healthy food leads to fitness and unhealthy food lead to fatness. How could any sensible person not believe this, right? The piece that's missing is vibration and alignment. Your alignment plays an important part in how well your body metabolizes your food, healthy or not. That's one reason my alignment became my number one priority. I knew without that piece—without learning how to be happy—I would not be able to sustain the body and fitness level I wanted."

Melissa explains how she approaches food today. "If it's what I consider to be a 'healthy' meal, I tell myself, 'This is soooooooo good for my body. The weight just drops off me when I nourish my body this way.' When the meal or snack is what I would typically consider nutritionally 'unhealthy,' but I'm having a craving for it, then I tell myself, 'This food is feeding my soul. My body wants a treat right now, and my cells know exactly what to do with this food. This food is fueling my spirit and I will savor every bite!'"

"Before I started on this transformation journey, I had a belief that my metabolism was slow—slow to lose weight and quick to gain weight," Melissa continues. "Since I've been telling a *new* story, one that includes how my alignment speeds up my metabolism, and how the weight just falls off me, my entire experience has changed!" In just a little over a year, Melissa has gone from 189 to 154 pounds. This is her lowest weight in 26 years. Recently she was surprised when she fit into size 8 slacks. "I was excited to fit into those pants. I couldn't believe it! The thing is, though, I don't want people to think it's about the numbers. We are each different, and no size or number on a scale is the 'right' number. Getting fit is what I desired for myself. This is what makes me happy. I think each person has to find what's right for them and discover the resources to help them get there. For me, it was understanding how the Law of Attraction works, listening to Abraham and implementing some of the tools Abraham talks about into my daily life."

Melissa's Five Steps

STEP 1
Make Alignment Your #1 Priority
In the beginning, you may find yourself jumping in and out of alignment. That's normal. Today I try to hover around "happy" as much as I can. I feel that anything I want in life, including physical fitness, is within reach when I'm practicing alignment. There are different levels of happiness, and I'm not saying I'm ecstatic all the time. Alignment includes a sense of well-being and an eagerness about what's to come. It is definitely in your best interest to pursue it.

STEP 2
Love Yourself (and Your Body)
Know your worth. I don't care who you are, you are worthy. You need to figure out how to love yourself and your body. It's somewhat emotional for me to say these words because it took me 50 years to get to this point, and I have to tell myself repeatedly that I am worth it because I never believed it before. It's okay to love yourself, and it's okay to love your body. It may take you a little while to figure out how to get there, but you can do it. When you practice these steps, you will be guided all the way.

STEP 3
Practice Positive Self-Talk
Supportive self-talk is extremely important. Women, in my opinion, are programmed to do things for everyone else but themselves. We must learn to re-program ourselves. We must learn to take care of ourselves without guilt and shame. We need to learn how to talk to ourselves in a way that empowers us. I say empowering things to myself all the time, such as, "I deserve to feed myself properly. I deserve to move my body

217

and exercise. I deserve to go on vacations. I deserve to make a lot of money. I deserve to wear nice clothes. I deserve to be loved. I deserve to love myself." Positive self-talk also comes in handy when you find yourself criticizing your weight or your food. I've turned my self-talk completely around and rarely criticize these things anymore.

STEP 4
Practice Scripting
Often before I go to bed, I will script what my next day is going to look like. I write out how I would like things to unfold, and I practice getting that feeling of accomplishment before it actually happens. (Abraham describes the Scripting process in the *Ask and It Is Given* book.) I pretend I am a screenplay writer who is detailing various scenes for my movie. The point is to write it down on paper or on your computer. (I find writing it down on paper feels better.) You can write a story about going to a department store and fitting into a smaller-sized dress. You can write a story about how you got inspired to start walking every day. You can write a story about how the weight just seems to fall off or how you found love. If you want to go general and simply say, "Tomorrow is going to be an amazing day," you can write that story too. Or you can be very specific, such as, "Tomorrow I am going to sell a house, and I am going to celebrate by taking my daughter out to dinner." I've had amazing things happen as a result of scripting. It's not that things turn out exactly as I imagined—sometimes they turn out even better!

STEP 5
Meditate

When I was at my old job, part of my routine was to start meditating in the morning as soon as my alarm went off. I would put my headphones on and do a guided meditation. With my current job, it's becoming more hit-and-miss, so I'm now meditating in the evening before bed. Meditation is so important because it connects you with your higher self. This is the energy you want to embrace because it gives you shortcuts to your desires. And who doesn't love a good shortcut?

Amber's Story
Learning to Forgive Yourself

I've released a total of 140 pounds, and I feel so much better. I now know that loving myself is a big part of the solution.

When Amber was 17, she reached her highest weight of 405 pounds and began to make the connection between her emotional eating and her anxiety. "I think my anxiety stemmed from a multitude of things," says Amber, now 30. "For one, I didn't have a good home life growing up. My father was verbally abusive. He was overly critical about lots of things, including how much I ate. I'm thankful I don't blame him for any of my challenges anymore, but it's definitely been a gradual process."

When Amber was 12, she was in and out of hospitals for a year due to relentless vomiting, and the doctors couldn't figure out the cause. They finally told her it was stress related. "Looking back, their prognosis makes sense," Amber says. "However, at the time, my parents and I were very confused, and we never took any steps to address my anxiety. As I got older, I just figured that this is who I am and there's not much I can do about it."

Amber had a tough time at college because of her weight. Her classes were spread out around campus, and walking was a struggle. Her knees hurt, and she would get out of breath easily. "My anxiety and emotional eating seemed to be getting worse in college," she recalls. "I eventually left and moved back home. I later enrolled in another school where I studied Aesthetics, which is what I really wanted to do in the first place."

One day, the instructor at the Aesthetics school showed the class *The Secret*, a film about the Law of Attraction. Skeptical at first, Amber found herself slowly getting drawn into the premise of the movie. By the time the film was over, she felt as if her mind had been split in two. "On one hand, the idea that we create our own reality with our thoughts sounded utterly insane, and on the other, there were scientists in the movie backing up these theories," Amber shares. Weeks later, she started asking herself questions such as, "Could it be I created my circumstances with my thoughts? If that is true, what would happen if I started thinking differently?"

Amber set out on a path to do just that: change her thinking. She made a decision to begin filling her mind with empowering thoughts. Eager for anything that would help her retrain her brain to see herself and her body in a better light, she began a journey to learn how to love herself. She also focused on a vision of how she wanted to look. In two years, Amber's inner dialogue had transformed, and so had her body. She released 80 pounds, which brought her to 325 pounds. Not only could she move around better, she felt more attractive and confident. Also present was the possibility she could meet her goal of getting below 200 pounds one day.

Then something unexpected happened. Amber learned she had Type 2 diabetes, and everything seemed to come to a screeching halt. The news hit her hard because it made her feel as if she had failed. She went right back to her old ways of thinking, blaming herself for getting diabetes. Whether it was true or not, she felt her eating habits and weight caused it. "My positive mindset took a blow," says Amber. "I felt like my life was over. All those feelings of not being good enough returned, and my dream of getting below 200 pounds took a nosedive."

"Instead of focusing on how my dad and both my grandmothers were diabetic, so it runs in the family, I blamed myself," shares Amber. She spiraled back into anxiety and depression. Now instead of beating herself up for being overweight, she was beating herself up for being overweight *and* diabetic.

"Still, once you learn about the Law of Attraction, you can't unlearn it," says Amber. "I kept going back to it. I kept searching, and one day while I was watching Law of Attraction videos on how to reverse Type 2 diabetes, an Abraham video showed up and really got my attention. Then another Abraham video popped up, and then another and another, and I watched each one more intently than the last. While watching, I had that same feeling as when I saw *The Secret* for the first time. I started becoming hopeful again." Every day, Amber watched Abraham videos on weight loss, diabetes, anxiety and more. She says these videos, along with Abraham-Hicks books, changed her life.

"I realized that my body is listening to everything I'm saying, so why would I keep bombarding it with negativity?" continues Amber. "If I were to tell my best friend, 'You're fat. You're no good. You gave yourself diabetes because you're lazy and have no willpower,' I'm pretty sure that friend would run the other way and never look back. Yet, this is how I treated myself. I beat myself up all the time. I was my own worst enemy. Listening to Abraham helped me change all that."

Once she focused on replacing those belittling conversations in her head with more soothing ones, the weight began to come off. "I've now lost a total of 140 pounds, and I feel so much better," Amber says with a smile. "I still have a way to go to get below the 200 mark, but I know that loving myself is the secret."

Amber's 5 Steps

STEP 1
Listen to Your Body

Sometimes I would work until 10pm and eat my dinner when I got home. I used to criticize myself for eating so late until I spoke with a nutritionist who said, "If you're hungry, eat. Maybe choose to have something light if that will make you feel better, but eat something. That's your body communicating to you that it's hungry." This was a big lesson for me because I never trusted my body before. Now I listen to my body. And if I'm hungry, I eat and don't beat myself up about it.

STEP 2
Love Your Body

I did a lot of mirror work when I started on my journey. If I looked in the mirror and didn't like what I saw, or if I thought negative thoughts like, "You look ugly," or "You look fat," I would say five things that I liked about myself to replace that one negative thought. I might say something like, "Even if you are overweight, that's not who you are. That doesn't define you." I would encourage anyone reading this to start appreciating your body for all the things it's done for you over the years. Start being thankful instead of critical.

STEP 3
Improve Your Self-Talk

My brain was on a self-criticism loop that played all day long, maybe even while I slept. Retraining my opinions of "me" set my self-love wheels in motion. It opened the door to all the other steps. I couldn't listen to my body, learn to love myself or even begin to understand how I could be successful at *anything* as long as those negative tapes were playing.

STEP 4
Rewrite Your Story

As a child, my mom used to tell me that no matter how much I ate, I never got full. I used to tell that story a lot. For some weird reason, I was somewhat proud of it. It wasn't until later on that I realized this story is not true. I do get full! I decided to create a new story. The new story is, "I love and enjoy my food and get full like everybody else. I also stop eating when I've had enough." You can make up whatever story you want, as long as it feels good when you tell it!

STEP 5
Visualize the Body You Want

I'm a huge fan of visualization. I often lie in bed and visualize my dream body and life. I imagine myself in my dream house walking around in my dream body. I imagine what it's like to finally get below the 200-pound mark, and I can't wait until that happens! (I'm getting close.) Visualization is very powerful, but I think you have to find a way to visualize that works for you. Some people have vision boards, others close their eyes and picture what they want and others write down what they want on paper. The important thing is to create the vision and focus on it consistently.

Val's Story
We Are What We Think

You have a lot more power than you think you do.
And that power is your thoughts.

V al, 51, a nurse for most of her career, gained weight when she found herself at a desk job. She accepted the position as executive director of an assisted living facility, thinking the change would do her good. While she enjoyed some aspects of the new job, she found it challenging to sit all day when she was usually on her feet as a nurse. In addition, her new career came with a great deal of unexpected stress.

"I think there were multiple reasons I gained weight," Val recalls. "Stress played a big part. It raises your cortisol levels, which makes you crave more junk food. I was also doing a lot of sitting. In addition, as the director, I oversaw the kitchen staff who cooked homemade meals every day, and I found myself in the kitchen 'sampling' those meals quite often. I realize these were all beliefs I had about what causes weight gain, but as we know from the Law of Attraction, we get what we believe."

After a year-and-a-half at the assisted living facility, Val realized her sense of vitality had diminished. In addition, she was now 40 pounds heavier. Her clothes didn't fit, and she didn't like the way she looked. She knew she wanted to get back to her normal weight of 145. Val had always been on the thin side, and at 5'10", she usually hovered around a size eight.

Familiar with Abraham-Hicks' teachings, Val knew releasing pounds was more about a change in mindset than it was about a change in diet. "Abraham says if you think that piece of cake is going to make you fat, then it will," shares Val. "I looked at my beliefs around food, and I realized these beliefs weren't serving me. So I made a decision to take on beliefs that would support me in releasing pounds while eating what I wanted. I wasn't interested in giving up the foods I loved. The last thing I wanted was to go on a diet because I didn't believe in diets. People who diet usually gain the weight back due to not learning how to develop new ways of thinking or because they have negative beliefs about their bodies or their worth. These beliefs become self-fulfilling prophecies."

Val decided she was going to release the 40 pounds while eating foods she loved, and she called it her Law of Attraction experiment. "I teach Law of Attraction and EFT (Emotional Freedom Technique) in addition to my professions in the medical field, and I wanted to be able to tell people that the Law of Attraction works. I wanted to tell my students that you can release pounds using Law of Attraction, and the reason I know this is because I did it myself," she explains.

Visualization is one of the tools Val used to release pounds. She visualized what it would feel like to get back down to 145. "I visualized the coming day when I would fit back into the very jeans I'm wearing right now," says Val. "I would stand in front of the mirror and imagine how excited I would be when those pants finally fit again. I rarely got on the scale, but every time I would think about the scale, I would imagine the number reading 145. I knew I had to believe that I was already 145 pounds before I could actually manifest it. Autumn arrived and in November, I put the pants on and they fit! I was super excited!"

Val also used visualization on her thighs. "I grew up believing that my thighs were big and ugly, and when I gained weight, all those beliefs seemed to resurface," she recounts. "Throughout my life, my family members would remind me that when I was little, my mother had to special-order my rubber pants because my thighs were so big. I know they weren't trying to be mean—they just thought it was funny. They would say things like, 'You're so tall and thin now, but you had these really chubby legs when you were little.' I hated my thighs and called them thunder thighs."

It was time to learn how to love herself, thighs and all. Val knew this recent weight gain revealed previous insecurities about her body were still there. She understood enough about Law of Attraction to know if she was going to beat herself up, visualization would not work, so she focused on accepting and loving her thighs. At other times during her day, she would visualize how she wanted her thighs to look. "Visualization is extremely powerful," Val says. "But it can only work when you are practicing acceptance."

In 10 months, Val let go of 31 of the 40 pounds she wanted to release, fit into her jeans and went back to nursing. "I have new things I want to manifest," says Val. "I still want to release another 10-15 pounds, eat healthier and lower my BMI (body mass index), but the main thing today is I feel good about myself. I'm especially excited that I get to share with others that I released weight through Law of Attraction. It just reinforces the fact that we are what we think."

Val's 5 Steps

STEP 1
Study the Law of Attraction
When you first encounter the Law of Attraction, you learn that everything you've been told about how the world works may not actually be true. With this new knowledge, you realize you have a lot more power than you thought you did. And that power is your thoughts. So whether you want to create an exotic vacation or the releasing of 50 pounds, understanding how Law of Attraction works will help you manifest it.

STEP 2
Identify Your Beliefs About Food and Weight
Your beliefs are choreographing the entire show. That's why it's so important to know what you believe about food and your body. Sometimes you'll choose to change your beliefs, and other times you'll choose to work with your beliefs. It just depends on which is easier. What do you believe about food and weight?

STEP 3
Accept and Love Your Body (All of It)
You may decide you would like to release pounds, build muscle or make changes to your body in some other way. It is very difficult to achieve any of these when you are not accepting your current body. Love your body now. Find reasons to appreciate it. Without this step, you remain stuck.

STEP 4
Visualize
Visualize, visualize, visualize.

STEP 5
Understand It's Not About the Food

I have goals and desires about the continued changes I would like to make to my body. Regardless of any action I take, the most powerful factors affecting my ability to achieve *anything* are my beliefs and my thoughts.

Robin's Story
Not All Emotional Eating Is Bad

When you eat from a feeling of joy, your body digests your food in a way that benefits your it. It's the emotion of joy that matters most.

R obin knows what it's like to be obsessed with food and weight and to frequently partake in emotional eating. "Food became my comfort, my escape, my only friend for nearly a decade," says the 43-year-old Canadian single mother. "Things finally shifted, and I released 68 pounds in the last four years. For the first two years, I still had that diet and deprivation consciousness. I released some pounds, but it was always a struggle. Then I enrolled in the Institute of Integrative Nutrition and discovered Abraham-Hicks around the same time. I became a huge fan of Abraham and listened continually. As a result of these two activities, my beliefs about weight, nutrition and the human body totally transformed—and so did my own body."

Robin knows emotions play a big part in weight gain. "People are always worried about calories and nutrition, but they're not concerned with how their emotions affect their bodies," she says. "Once I started releasing anger, resentment and fear—no longer carrying all these negative emotions around with me—the weight started to drop off."

Robin began gaining weight in her early twenties after she was married, going from a size 10 to a size 22 in women's clothing within a six-year span. When she became pregnant, she developed diabetes, high blood pressure and high cholesterol. "Now that's all gone," shares Robin. "I'm off all medications, and my sugar, blood pressure and cholesterol are within normal ranges. At age 43, I'm in better shape mentally, physically, energetically and spiritually than when I was in my 20s. I went from 228 to 160 pounds by following the Abraham style of eating, and my body has completely transformed. I put my alignment first and as a result, I can eat whatever I want. True, I don't have the desire to eat like I used to because I'm happier and take better care of myself now."

The best part of Robin's transformation, she explains, is she doesn't feel negative emotion about her food choices anymore. "There's so much shame and guilt around food, and I wish that could end," Robin says. "When you eat from a feeling of shame and guilt, your body digests your food in a way that does not benefit you. Feelings of shame and guilt turn into stress, resulting in raised cortisol levels that create fat on the body. Also, shame and guilt lead to negative emotional eating, which creates more shame and guilt, and the cycle perpetuates itself. The key is to learn how to soothe yourself and soften that critical voice in your head. The more you soothe yourself, the less shame and guilt you'll experience."

Robin believes trusting her body and giving it what it wants is another key to success. She eats because she's hungry and because it feels joyful to do so. She believes that if the food feels joyful going in, it's going to provide her body with the nutrition and fuel she needs.

"It's also important to remember that not all emotional eating is bad," adds Robin. "We can't remove the emotion from eating, and we shouldn't. Food is fuel to keep our bodies going, but eating food can also be a joyous experience. It can be a fun experience. It can be a loving experience, and it should be all of those things. If we remove the emotions from eating, we take the joy out of it. When you eat from a feeling of joy, your body digests your food in a way that is *beneficial*. It's the joy that matters the most."

Robin admits she doesn't eat and exercise perfectly and that's okay with her. "I eat cookies and drink lots of coffee. I don't work out all the time. I do, however, love going to hot yoga. It's all about love for me—I have to be doing things I love," she emphasizes. "If I love the cookie, I love the cookie. I don't care if the cookie has a lot of sugar. If I want it, I'm going to have it. If the donut is tasty, I'm eating the donut. It's not going to turn into a pound of fat because I don't have those extreme fears anymore. Am I conscious about nutrition? Yes. Most of the time, I like to eat what I consider healthy foods. I eat a plant-based diet because that's what my body now craves and because that fits with my current beliefs. My body and mind want foods that come straight from the earth. But I know that my emotional state/vibration while eating is more important than the actual food I'm putting in my mouth. It is my vibration that determines how my body uses the food."

As far as figuring out an eating style, Robin recommends developing your connection with your Inner Being. From there, you can practice trusting the messages you receive. "You've got to find what works for you," she clarifies. "I nurture my connection with my Inner Being every day. That connection is sacred to me. And then I follow the guidance I receive. As a result, I trust myself. I don't second-guess myself anymore. I eat what I love, exercise when I want and don't think about weight loss or fat or calories anymore. I eat for joy and to stay alive. I don't believe in trying to get to a certain size or number on a scale," she continues, "but if that works for you, then go for it. Personally, I hope we can one day live in a world where everyone eats for joy and love and gives up caring about how much they weigh or what size they are."

Robin's 5 Steps

STEP 1
Connect

The first thing I do every morning is sit down and have coffee with my Inner Being. I'll sit in my sacred spot, get quiet and connect with Source. The number one thing is feeling that connection and doing whatever promotes that. I'm not really a huge meditator. I go to hot yoga almost every day, and that's an hour of being in the zone. I talk to my Inner Being during yoga, and that's another way I connect. I actually feel that my entire life is one big request for connection.

STEP 2
Practice Appreciation

I regularly write appreciation lists. I usually carry a journal (my "Good Things Book") with me wherever I go. I look around and appreciate everything in my life as best I can, and as I write those things down, I shift my energy. I write positive aspects about my kids, my body and life in general. Appreciation is a powerful tool that leads to alignment and feeling connected to my Inner Being. If you feel yourself getting frustrated or spiraling into negativity, think of things you appreciate. Write them down if you can, and feel your energy shift.

STEP 3
Stop Criticizing Yourself

How do you talk to yourself? When you look in the mirror, are you happy with yourself or are you criticizing your appearance? Whatever you say to yourself is what you put out to the Universe. And as we know, our thoughts attract our experience. Once you begin to shift your negative thoughts about yourself to more positive ones, you will attract more positive experiences. But if you keep telling yourself you are fat and unattractive, that's what you are going to keep experiencing. Change your self-talk, and your whole life will transform.

STEP 4
Love Your Body
Find a way to love your body in a way that makes you joyful. What can you do to honor your body and show it you love it? Maybe it's a massage or a facial. Maybe exercising is your way of showing love to your body. Whatever you do, make sure your expression of love is from a gentle place and not from a place of forced action. Wait for the inspiration. Once you start connecting with your Inner Being and improving your self-talk, you will eventually be inspired to express love and appreciation to your body. It will come. Just be patient.

STEP 5
Eat for Joy
When you're eating, how are you feeling? Are you feeling joy when you eat? Or are you eating unconsciously, not feeling anything? Are you eating quickly because you're in a rush, not tasting or enjoying the food before you? Are you eating because you're depressed, stressed out or tired? Your mood is important when you are eating. When your body digests your food from a place of joy, only good can come from it. On the flip side, when you find yourself eating for reasons other than hunger and joy, be easy on yourself. Love yourself, soothe yourself and be aware of your self-talk.

Gianna's Story
Letting Go

I knew I wanted to feel beautiful and worthy of love, and that's ultimately what I was craving.

Even though Gianna, now 24, was only a size six when she was 18, she still wanted to lose weight. "I was always insecure about my body growing up, especially when I was old enough to start dating," shares Gianna. "I just didn't feel attractive."

"Three years ago, people couldn't understand why I wanted to lose weight, and that's fine. Body image is a personal thing," Gianna says. She had already come a long way mentally, physically and spiritually, having struggled with anorexia when she was 18. She had even developed orthorexia, becoming super obsessed with eating healthy. She experienced panic attacks about food and weight and would regularly break down and cry.

"Back then, I followed one crazy diet after another, no matter how restrictive and unsustainable," Gianna recalls. "I kept trying to implement all kinds of diet tips. I read something about not eating after 7pm, and I started doing that along with forcing myself to drink massive amounts of water and attempting to work out twice-a-day. It was from a place of, 'I need to change myself and then maybe I'll have some self-esteem.' I actually got down to 93 pounds and stopped menstruating because I didn't have enough body fat. Eventually my digestive system was compromised to the point where I couldn't keep anything down, even water!"

Gianna finally reached the breaking point where she said to herself, "All right, is this how you want to live your life? Is this how you want to feel? Is this who you want to be, because this will probably get worse!" She wanted to be healthy and have a great relationship with her body, doing it in a way that was sustainable. "I knew I wanted to feel beautiful and worthy of love, and that's ultimately what I was craving," she reveals. There had to be a better way. It was exhausting to be so hard on herself all the time.

She proceeded to do a lot of spiritual, mindset and emotional work around how she talked to herself and treated herself. Gianna listened to Abraham-Hicks and other teachers while examining her beliefs about weight loss, fitness and body image. She realized it was crucial that she become receptive to wellness.

"I kept hearing Abraham-Hicks talk about how well-being is our dominant state," Gianna continues. "If this is true, which I believe it is, do I really think a taco or an ice cream cone can overcome the wellness of Source that flows through my body? The answer is no, I don't. There's so much evidence of this well-being. When you scratch your arm and it bleeds, your cells automatically go into repair mode and eventually the scratch is completely healed. Our bodies naturally lean towards wellness and thriving, but we get in the way with our beliefs of limitation and struggle."

Gianna basically transformed her relationship with weight by focusing on her body's dominant state of well-being. "I began to believe that it really is safe to let go and not have to control everything so much," she says. She learned it's safe to follow her joy, knowing she's always going to be led to the food and exercise that will feel good to her.

She began to believe it was okay to have what she desires, whether it's a pastry or a salad. "It's all allowed because I trust my body, knowing that it's intelligent enough to ask for what it needs in order to thrive. If it's asking for a certain food, there's something in there that it wants, and I'm no longer going to deprive my body of that. I'm not going to feel guilty about it either," she emphasizes.

Today Gianna is a size two and considers that to be her happy place. She lost 30 pounds three years ago and has kept it off without stress and deprivation. "Lately I've been eating a lot of avocado toast and protein cookies," she says. "They taste good, and they're what I've been craving. In the past, I had so many restrictions: no sugar, no gluten, no oil, etc. Now I eat what I want and trust my body to get what it wants from the food. I am a vegan, but that's more of a spiritual decision than a dietary one."

It took about a year for Gianna to lose the 30 pounds while practicing new ways of thinking about food and her body. (This practice is on-going.) She recalls, "I definitely shifted my reactions around food. Even though I was working out less and eating more of what I wanted, the weight was slowly melting off and never came back. Now my weight doesn't fluctuate more than a few pounds. For me, a big plus is not only getting to my happy place with my weight but also getting to a feeling of freedom around the subject. I'm not worried about food and my weight anymore. Food doesn't control me. That's not something I experienced before, and it feels really good."

Gianna's 5 Steps

STEP 1
Trust Your Body

Your body knows what it needs to thrive. When you worry about what you're eating, or when you're trying to stick to the perfect diet, you're not listening to your body. When you truly listen to and trust your body, you feel calmer. You feel happier and more in tune with a higher vibration. You have less stress, and this helps your body express radiant well-being. Trust your body, and trust that your body is meant to be well.

STEP 2
Give Yourself Freedom

Follow your inspiration. Don't force yourself to exercise or eat things you really don't want to eat. The more you allow the expression of freedom in your life, the more joy you will feel. Allowing the good into your life, including the body and the love you want, is easy when you relax and let go of those things you are trying so hard to control or force. Your natural state is a sensation of freedom, so anything less doesn't feel good.

STEP 3
Stop Feeling Guilty

If you ate something you think you shouldn't have eaten, try to feel better about it. Don't get all crazy. Let it go. The same applies to working out. If you decided to work out and wound up bingeing on Netflix instead, let it go. Guilt is a useless emotion with zero benefits. Learn how to talk to yourself in a supportive way instead. When I was anorexic, I tortured myself with hundreds of guilty and fearful thoughts about myself. I turned that around. Now I talk to myself like

I'm coaching one of my clients. I treat myself with love and respect and don't guilt myself.

STEP 4
Create a New Story
Abraham-Hicks talks a lot about creating a new story, and that's what I did. I had many beliefs around food, my body and weight that were damaging my health. Changing your story is the same thing as changing your beliefs. I knew I had to change my beliefs and create a new narrative around food. You can tell what your story is by what you say either in your head or to other people. What do you worry about or complain about? That's the story you want to transform.

STEP 5
Ditch Deprivation
In my experience, the more restrictive the diet, the more out of control I felt. I don't believe deprivation is healthy. It definitely wasn't for me because the more I told myself I couldn't have something, the more I wanted it. It's the opposite of freedom and trust, making it very difficult to feel joyful. When you learn to trust yourself, you no longer need to rely on the short-lived benefits of strict rules and regimented diets.

Audrey's Story

Visualize Your Desired Body into Existence

Visualization works because it's the fastest way to transform your beliefs.

Since Audrey, now 59, was a pre-teen, she never felt attractive. In the early 1960s, Twiggy—the extremely thin (like a twig) super model—was the role model for girls. As Audrey got older, she felt the body she wanted was always out of reach—25 pounds out of reach to be exact. She started dieting when she was a teenager, trying everything from appetite suppressants to B12 shots, the cabbage soup diet and many more. None of them worked.

Audrey carried a lot of guilt and frustration in relation to her body and food. She felt guilty about what she ate, how much she ate and when she ate it. Married in her late twenties, Audrey was happy with her husband but unhappy with herself. Throughout the years, she read many books about the power of our thoughts, including *You Can Heal Your Life* by Louise Hay, but it wasn't until 2017 that she discovered *The Gabriel Method* by Jon Gabriel and the teachings of Abraham-Hicks. "Something was beginning to click," says Audrey. "It's as if I realized that all the books I read over the years were saying the same thing: We create our reality with our thoughts and emotions."

Audrey became fascinated with visualization, something both Gabriel and Abraham-Hicks recommend highly. While taking walks, Audrey would visualize her slim body at her desired weight of 120 pounds. She felt joy and increased energy every time she practiced visualization and started having fun with it! She became gradually more detailed with her visualizations, feeling her belly getting flatter and her hips getting smaller as she walked. As her joy expanded, her weight decreased. Her mantra became, *I want to shed anything that's not the real me.*

Audrey also started asking her Inner Being to guide her to the foods that were right for her. She focused on what she was *giving* her body instead of what she was *denying* it and visualized being healthy and choosing good food. It has now been two years since Audrey released 25 pounds within six months and went down three clothing sizes.

"One of the important things about visualization is the detail," Audrey explains. "I visualized my perfect body down to the size and shape I wanted to be. I did these visualizations while I walked and hiked in the woods, and this alone time allowed me to tune into my desires and act as if I had already achieved my goals. I would feel slimmer right on the spot. During my walks, I got in touch with my Inner Being and eventually was guided to eat whole foods, although I do indulge in pizza and baked goods occasionally. It's wonderful that there's no effort anymore around food and weight. My Inner Being knows how to guide me to where I want to go. I just have to get happy, know what I want and follow my impulses."

"Just today I allowed myself a piece of coconut cake," continues Audrey. "I normally would only eat a bite or two. Before I ate it, I affirmed that my body would know exactly what to take from it and release the rest. I affirmed that it was good for me, and I enjoyed every bite."

When Audrey is deciding what she would like to eat or sits down for a meal, she stops herself when she has a thought such as "I shouldn't eat that" or "That's bad for me." Instead she says, "I deserve to enjoy my food without hating myself. My body knows what to do with this food and will convert it into beneficial energy and nutrients, and I appreciate that." If, after she finishes eating, she notices any sort of guilt popping up again, she stops and focuses on the beauty and light in her life, and trusts the process.

"Visualization works because it's the fastest way to transform your beliefs," says Audrey. "I am in a few groups where people often complain about their weight. I tell them, 'You still think you're the fat girl.' There's nothing wrong with being the fat girl, but if that's something you want to change, then you need to visualize how you want to look. That's my message to anyone wanting to transform anything. You must see it and believe it before you can manifest it, and visualization is the most effective way to do that. Visualization helps you create new beliefs about yourself and your body. If you don't change your beliefs, you're going to gain the weight back because Law of Attraction always gives you what you believe."

"If you're having a difficult time losing weight, it's likely because you can't see yourself in that new body," Audrey shares. "You haven't done the work to hold that vision and believe it as if it's a done deal—as if you *are* that now. If you don't believe it, then you don't have the power to create it. Instead, you believe you are a victim of your body. You believe your body betrays you and makes things difficult for you—not giving you what you want. That's what I once thought, that's what most people think and that's why there are a million-and-one different methods to lose weight. But those are all external ways to try to change while the solution is not external. It's internal and starts with your thoughts."

"You've got the key," Audrey insists. "We all do. It's right inside us. You can unlock the door now by changing your beliefs through visualization. It's all so very empowering."

Audrey's 5 Steps

STEP 1
Visualize

See in your mind's eye exactly how you want your body to look. Go deeper and imagine how you want your body to feel. Combining seeing and feeling during your visualizations will anchor that reality within your consciousness. The glue that holds it all together is the feel-good emotions you experience as you visualize. It's all part of the process; seeing your body, feeling your body and experiencing the resulting emotions. For example, if you want to be a certain size, see and feel yourself as that size. Then visualize fitting into your new clothes and experience the joy as you move through the world with your healthy body.

STEP 2
Keep It Positive

When you think in terms of not having something, your body feels tension because that thought is not in alignment with your Inner Being, which always feels good. Keep reaching for the next best thought, aiming to make your way to a positive vibration. We all experience times of challenge and contrast, but you can move closer to the vortex when you recognize you've reacted negatively and can then choose a different feeling by choosing a different thought.

STEP 3
Get Excited and Have Fun!

See and feel that you have already achieved your goal and then get excited about it. Live in that excitement and use it to create fun. Joy and excitement vibrate at high frequencies and summon your desires with ease. Be playful with yourself. Embrace passion, empowerment, freedom, love and appreciation. Feel the deliciousness of these high-vibration feelings partnering with your excitement.

STEP 4
Listen to Your Internal Guidance
If you are guided to pick up a book or follow a particular program, do it! Your internal guidance, aka your Inner Being, is the true source of You! By paying attention, you will find you are being led to your best self. If the cacophony of life drowns out the inner wisdom, take time to sit quietly and allow the answers to emerge. Cultivate your relationship with your Inner Being and become aware of its nudges. It always has your best interest at heart and will never lead you astray.

STEP 5
Take the Process One Step at a Time
Don't rush it. Conscious creation takes time. It will gradually all come together. Focus on the steps that come next in your journey, not all the steps spread out before you. See the path, not the mountain. This enables you to celebrate along the way and experience more joy during the process. Whatever your approach may be, appreciating each minor accomplishment will fuel you to success, and you will find the balance that leads to your best life and body.

Starla's Story
Sometimes No Plan Is the Best Plan

Despite being someone who outlines every move to the last detail, Starla had no plan. This was uncharted territory.

At one time, Starla, 56, had a drama-free life. She married a military man and had two children by the time she was 19. She lived all over the world including California, South Dakota, Florida and England. Life was good.

After 22 years of near-bliss, Starla experienced what she calls a surprise divorce. "It got ugly. I definitely didn't see it coming. I had just turned 40, and the only good thing about it was my kids were grown and out of the house, so they didn't have to witness the craziness."

Starla eventually moved back to Oregon to be closer to her parents and found a job working for city government. That's when she started gaining weight for the first time in her adult life. Always a small woman at 5', she would usually fluctuate between 103 and 135 pounds. "I may have gotten up to 150 at one point, but I had been able to lose it quickly," says Starla. "But at the new job, I often over-indulged in donuts and sweets because I was bored out of my mind. A lot of people ask why I stayed so long in a job I hated. The short answer is, I liked the money. But I was unhappy and it showed. The work environment wasn't a healthy one, and the job wasn't challenging. I kept getting fatter and fatter. I remember telling myself, 'There's nothing wrong with being fat and happy,' but after gaining 70 pounds, I realized that was a lie. The truth was that the job was sucking the life out of me. The only thing I enjoyed was my family and my new husband."

Drinking beer at night was another way Starla coped with the frustrations of her job. "The more I drank, the more I ate, and the more I ate, the fatter I got," Starla recalls. It got to the point where she stopped looking in the mirror because every time she did, she would think, "What are you doing to yourself? Look at how fat you are! You look terrible." Starla recognized there was a lot of self-hatred going on, but she didn't know how to stop it.

When her mom had back surgeries last year, Starla decided to take a two-month medical leave to help her mom recover. Even though it was hard seeing her mother in pain, she enjoyed being away from the office. During the leave, Starla began listening to Abraham-Hicks. The videos inspired her to ask questions about what she really wanted. She found herself pondering, "I have so many things to be grateful for. I'm surrounded by people who love me. Why am I so unhappy?"

Eventually Starla felt guided to start meditating again as she had once done. The meditations helped her remember the premise of the Law of Attraction: we create our own realities. After a few weeks of meditating, Starla felt inspired to make a vision board. On the board, she placed photos from magazines that represented a new job, a smaller body, vacations, a new vehicle and more. She also began visualizing. During her visualizations, she imagined experiencing the things she wanted and felt the feelings as if they were happening in the moment. She also remembered how it felt to be thin and what it would be like to love her work. Soon she manifested an Alaskan cruise and a recreational vehicle. Perhaps she would manifest her dream job and body as well!

As Starla enjoyed these daily meditations and visualizations, reality soon hit. It was time to return to work. Her new-found zest for life seemed to deflate in an instant. Starla went through the motions of performing her work tasks at the same desk and chair she sat in for nearly 11 years. She drove the same route, parked in the same parking spot, looked at the same computer screen, stared out the same window, ordered the same lunches and answered to the same boss. And then one day, after only two weeks, she stood up from her desk, marched into her boss's office and quit her job. It was one of the best things she has ever done for herself. An immediate sense of freedom washed over her entire body. Despite being someone who usually plans out every move and decision to the last detail, Starla had no plan and no plan to make a plan. This was uncharted territory.

At home, Starla continued meditating, adding pictures to her vision board and listening to Abraham-Hicks and other teachers. One day the phone rang and it was a girlfriend who was bursting with child-like enthusiasm and sharing how she lost 50 pounds on a particular food plan. The plan her friend spoke of intrigued Starla, especially since Starla had been trying to lose weight for years. After some research, she decided to give it a try. She didn't know if this was *the* step that would help her reach her goal, but she definitely felt guided to pursue it. Trusting her Inner Guidance was something she was beginning to get a handle on. The meditations and visualizations were aiding her to get to that place of knowing, and she couldn't help but think that just maybe this call from her friend was a sign from her higher self.

In four months, Starla has released 30 pounds. "You wouldn't think losing 30 pounds would make such a difference," she shares, "but I feel completely changed. I have more energy and I feel so empowered. I want to release another 30 pounds, but I understand that it's a gradual process. I love how I'm listening to my body and seeking guidance in meditation. I now know that dieting never worked because I didn't have my head in the right place. I was trying to deprive myself of food without doing the important work, which is connecting with my Inner Being."

As for the perfect job, Starla believes that path is beginning to reveal itself. Her dad has since made his transition, and it is likely Starla's mom will soon move in with her and her husband and Starla will become her caretaker. "I want to take care of my mom, but I also sense there's something else calling me as well," she says. "I'm just not sure what it is, and I'm okay with that because I know I'll be guided every step of the way."

Starla's 5 Steps

STEP 1
Get Your Mind in the Right Place
It's important to realize you are connected to something bigger than yourself. We are more than our bodies and our egos. If we can connect our hearts to our deepest wishes, we can attract our deepest desires.

STEP 2
Meditate
Meditation is one of the ways you connect with your higher self. This connection provides the access to a knowing that transcends this physical plane. Tapping into this all-knowingness will help you with whatever you are struggling with, including releasing pounds.

STEP 3
Visualize
We have been given the gift of imagination for a reason. Most of us stop using it when we begin to grow up, but that is not to our benefit. Use visualization to create whatever it is you want in your life. It is one of the most efficient tools.

STEP 4
Appreciate
Appreciation raises your vibration. You can't be sad, angry or depressed when you are in a state of appreciation. When you appreciate and love your body, you will open the door to new ideas and inspiration to help support you in making any changes you want to make.

STEP 5
Listen to Your Body

As we got older, we learned to distrust our bodies and ourselves. We learned to doubt our decisions and our feelings. The more we practice meditation, the more we realize we can trust ourselves and our bodies. We can trust our body's hunger signals and its cravings. It's a wonderful, calming feeling to learn how to trust your body again!

Snober's Story
Listening to Your Body

I take much longer to decide what to eat now because I try to figure out what my body wants. I also have learned to trust the answers I receive.

Extremes. That's how Snober, a 29-year-old math teacher in Austin, Texas, describes her past relationship with food and her body. She was either bingeing or dieting. As a result, she would gain 30, 40 or even 50 pounds in less than a year, only to begin a strict dieting regimen to try to lose it. "I was always worried that once I reached my fitness goal, which I often did, I wouldn't be able to maintain it," she recalls. "How could I? I didn't know how."

Her parents, fearful that Snober would gain too much weight like her older brother, often criticized her food choices during Snober's pre-teen years. In middle school, Snober became aware she had low self-esteem. When she was 12 years old, she asked her mother if she was supposed to love herself. Her mother replied, "Of course you're supposed to love yourself!" "But how?" Snober wondered. The answer would elude her for years to come.

When Snober was 26, she was in a difficult relationship with a Turkish man. Her parents, with whom she lived at the time (it was part of their Pakistani culture for a daughter to live with her parents until she married), did not approve. They wanted her to date and marry a Pakistani man and complained when Snober was out with her boyfriend, while her boyfriend complained when she was home with her parents! "I gained so much weight during that time," shares Snober. "I'm an emotional eater. Actually I should stop saying that because I'm not an emotional eater anymore, but I used to be, and anytime I would get upset, angry or sad, I would go on a binge and then have horrible regret afterwards. Plus I felt physically ill from all the food. I did a lot of bingeing while I was in that relationship."

Snober finally got her own apartment 15 minutes away from her parents, and that independence gave her some relief. She expected things to improve with her boyfriend now that she had more freedom, but that didn't happen, so she eventually ended things. That was one of the lowest, loneliest points in her life. She didn't have a good relationship with her family, and she no longer had a boyfriend. One positive thing, however, that came from living on her own was she began to focus on her spirituality. Wanting to connect with her Inner Being/God/Goddess, she started meditating. She also began searching YouTube for spiritual videos that inspired her. That's when she found Abraham-Hicks. "I still remember how that first Abraham video brought a smile to my face," she says. "I think it was the first time I smiled in months. It was a clip where Esther Hicks is moving her hand around in a circle talking about the vortex. I had no clue what the vortex was at the time, but I felt her enthusiasm."

It wasn't until two years ago that Snober started to apply what she was learning from Abraham to her desire to release pounds. She would post questions on Abraham-Hicks Facebook groups such as, "I've got a handle on everything else but my weight. How do I change my mindset?

How do I view my body differently?" Through the support she received from those groups and her own studies, Snober finally realized she needed to learn to love and accept her current body. "After I made that realization, after it really clicked, I made the decision to fall in love with myself," she explains. "Little by little, I began to see myself as beautiful. I kept focusing on loving and accepting myself and when I couldn't get there, I would focus on some totally different subject that made me feel good."

Snober released 25 pounds, and she's now at 142, maintaining it for over a year. "I think it all comes down to following your inspiration," she says. "You hear lots of Abraham people say, 'When you're aligned, you can eat whatever you want and you can still get fit,' but that's difficult for many of us to believe. I think it's a true statement, but I also know you have to work with your beliefs. My belief was that as I connected more and more with my Inner Being, I would be guided to the right steps for me in terms of my desire to get fit."

As it turns out, Snober was guided to what many might call intuitive eating. Her general method was to listen to her body. "I take much longer to decide what to eat now because I try to figure out what my body wants," she reveals. "I will look through my fridge and ask my body, 'Do you want this? Do you want that?' And I trust the answers I get. Sometimes I want something really healthy, and sometimes I want something sweet. Yesterday I was craving rotisserie chicken with a baked potato, steamed carrots and a glass of milk. I went to the store and bought all the items and enjoyed them so much. I felt as if my body was saying, 'Yes, yes, yes! This is exactly what we wanted!'"

Snober also learned how to enjoy her food more. "A lot of times when I think about eating, I'll ask myself, 'Am I really hungry?' I'm training myself to listen to my body before I start eating a meal. I also make sure I'm appreciating every single bite that I put in my mouth. Have you ever noticed that food stops tasting good when your body starts getting full?" she asks. "If, say, on a scale of one to 10, the first bite is a 10 and the current bite is a five, you know you're about to be full. The food is not going to taste as good anymore. Once I get that signal, I know my body is saying 'Okay, that's it. I don't really want anymore.' That's when I usually stop eating now."

When it comes to exercising, Snober is also learning how to listen to her Inner Guidance. "Sometimes, for example, when I have a lot of work to get done in a short amount of time, I might get the sudden urge to go for a jog," she shares. "I used to ignore those urges that seemed inconvenient or didn't make sense, and now I pay attention. It always works out in my favor when I follow my Inner Guidance. My entire life has changed. I'm much more confident inside and out. I've got an inner peace about me I didn't have before, and I'm so excited about what's next."

Snober's 5 Steps

STEP 1
Focus on What You Want
If you consistently focus on the things you don't like about your body, you will keep finding things to criticize. Try to avoid looking at the things that need improvement and focus on the things that are already improving. If you can't find anything yet, then focus on something entirely different that feels good to you. The point is to raise your vibration by thinking of whatever feels good. That affects everything for the better.

STEP 2
Love and Appreciate Your Body
You need to love yourself the way you are before you can start to make long-term changes. I noticed that men found me attractive, but I couldn't understand why because I was viewing myself through an unflattering lens. As I started to look for attractive aspects of my physique, I slowly began to fall in love with myself and my body. I realized that I was beautiful. My face, my hair, my body...all of it. In the beginning, whenever I looked in the mirror, all I saw were my flaws. Eventually I could look in the mirror and see my beauty.

STEP 3
Listen to Your Body
It's important to follow your inspiration in all things, including what to eat, when to eat, how much to eat and when to exercise. I never knew how to communicate with my body before. It seemed like a foreign concept. But how else do you know what to eat or when to stop eating? Try to get in touch with feeling good before eating. Raise your vibration as high as you can before you ingest anything, and it will

do miracles for you and your body. Sometimes this is not possible because you may still be eating to numb your feelings or for whatever reasons. That's okay. Move on as soon as you can and keep practicing. Keep managing your vibration so that you are feeling as good as possible whenever you eat.

STEP 4
Visualize

I keep pictures of myself when I was extremely fit, and I look at those every day for inspiration. I love to visualize and daydream about what I want, who I want to be with, my dream house and all of that. I simply close my eyes and think about what I want and how it's going to feel when I manifest it. Even if you believe you are not good at visualizing, remember that we were all given the gift of imagination. See if you can figure out how to access yours.

STEP 5
Remind Yourself of What You Know and Who You Are

It's important to keep reminding yourself of how the Law of Attraction works, especially when you're with people who aren't familiar with it. I'm very strong in my belief about Law of Attraction and Abraham-Hicks, and yet I can still get off-balance when something triggers me. For instance, let's say I go home for a visit and my mom expresses concern about the piece of chocolate cake I'm enjoying. If I haven't been meditating, I can easily fall back into old habits of thought, such as fear that the cake is going to make me gain weight. Keep practicing the steps that bring you the most happiness and clarity, so that when challenging situations arise, you'll be able to bounce back quickly.

Renee's Story
The Power of Allowing

Instead of trying to force a solution, I allowed a solution.

Renee, 47, was raised by her single mom, who she affectionately calls a hippie. "We lived just north of Salt Lake City in a very religious environment," says Renee. "We were always the weird ones because we weren't very religious. My mom was more spiritual, though she loved all religions. We used to tease her that she was a Catholic Jew because she worked for a Jewish catering company for many years."

Unlike her mother, Renee didn't love all religions because she didn't understand them. None of it made sense to her, so when she heard about the Law of Attraction when she was 16, she immediately became curious. She proceeded to read anything she could get her hands on about the subject and felt as if a door had opened to a new world of possibilities.

The first two books she read on the subject were *The Game of Life and How to Play It* by Florence Scovel Shinn and *The Magic of Thinking Big* by David J. Schwartz, PhD. She was then introduced to Wayne Dyer's books and years later to Esther and Jerry Hicks and the life-changing teachings of Abraham. That's when things really took off for her. The Abraham-Hicks book *Money and the Law of Attraction* transformed Renee's relationship with money. (She had grown up in poverty and didn't know anything different.) This book taught her how to attract abundance for herself and her family and also helped her with weight and health.

"I never had a problem with weight until after I had my two children," recalls Renee. "Seventeen years later, my husband and I realized we should probably do something, as we had gained weight together. We tried all sorts of diets, cutting out various foods, but nothing seemed to work. I'm a big researcher and found something wrong with every diet and just about every food. Eventually I got tired of thinking about what I was putting in my mouth, and so I just let it go."

For two years, Renee watched as her daughter and husband continued to search for the perfect diet. They tried the Whole30® Program, the Ketogenic Diet, low-carb and many more. "Meanwhile," she recalls, "I was still unhappy with my weight. I was 192 pounds, felt fat and lacked energy. It reached the point where we moved to Arizona five years ago because we wanted a healthier lifestyle. We wanted to find a way to feel better."

Once they were in Arizona, Renee started wondering why losing weight is so difficult when Abraham says life is supposed to be easy. She returned to her Abraham books and started focusing on alignment. "I believed I would attract a solution, and so I finally stopped worrying about my weight and food," she shares. "I tried to think of other things that made me feel good. I thought about my business. I thought about my daughters." Renee knew Abraham recommends changing the subject and thinking of something that brings happier feelings.

About three months later, Renee came home from an appointment when her husband had just started watching a documentary on Netflix called *What the Health*. Although tired, she agreed to watch it with him. At the end of the film, she looked at her husband and said, "This actually seems do-able." The documentary somehow made sense to Renee. It resonated with her, and no one was more surprised than she was.

"We actually started eating a plant-based diet," Renee explains. "While that may seem extreme to some people, it was easy for us. I eat more food than I've ever eaten in my life and feel excited about meals again. Sure, I had to learn a lot. For example, I didn't know what a lentil was! But I have to say that instead of it feeling like a chore, it's been fun and effortless. We were just going to try it as an experiment, but after that first week, I felt amazing. I've never felt that way in my entire life!" In less than a year, Renee has released 54 pounds and her husband has released 65.

"I totally believe that the success I've experienced with my weight and health is because I got into alignment about it," Renee clarifies. "Somewhere along the line, I forgot that the answer to everything is feeling good and letting go. When I remembered, I stopped searching for the perfect diet. I stopped pushing against everything by saying, 'I can't eat this and I can't eat that.' Feeling good became my priority again and instead of trying to force a solution, I allowed a solution. It turns out that solution was super easy to follow."

Previously, Renee never would have considered eating a plant-based diet. "I met people who had done it, and it seemed extreme to me," she commented. "Even being a vegetarian seemed extreme. But the Universe knows the path of least resistance, and when you let go, allowing the answers to come to you, they show up. They may not be the answers you expect, but it's about how they feel to you. Each person has to find what feels right to them. This answer felt right to us."

The next step for Renee is to build physical strength. "When I lost all the fat," she says, "I also lost muscle. I'm not interested in large muscles, but I am inspired to feel stronger. It's all about the inspiration. I'm going to keep listening and following where it takes me."

Renee's 5 Steps

STEP 1
Make Peace with Where You Are
When you don't make peace with where you are, you get stuck. You get in a cycle of trying to force solutions. Your focus is on what you don't want instead of what you do want. Making peace with your current body does not mean you can't also focus on your new body. You can do both and, in fact, you must if you want to attract any sort of change.

STEP 2
Be in the Moment
Our power is in the moment. So instead of worrying about the past or the future, focus on this moment. How are you feeling right now? What are you thinking right now? Worrying is the opposite of being present. If your current thought does not feel good, if it's not an empowering one, then how can you improve it? Meditate, visualize, do whatever you need to do to practice being in the moment.

STEP 3
Follow Your Inspiration
In order to follow your inspiration, you have to be able to hear it or feel it. When you are trying to force solutions, you are closing yourself off from your inspiration. Following your inspiration requires some amount of quieting your mind so you can allow the inspiration to come forth. The more you practice this, the more you will trust it.

STEP 4
Set the Intention
What do you want? How do you want to feel? Set an Intention. This is powerful because you are focusing on what you really want and letting the Universe respond. Sometimes your intention will change, and that's okay too, because that's how evolution and expansion work. One intention leads to another and leads to another, etc., so be flexible and open to setting new intentions when inspired to do so.

STEP 5
Change the Subject
When you just can't get to a better-feeling thought about a certain subject, it's time to think about something else that makes you feel better. For a long time, I was obsessed with finding the "right" diet, and this search was making me stressed and unhappy. I finally realized I had to let it go. I needed to change the subject. I needed to think of something else that felt good. Interestingly enough, when I let go, the solution came.

Cindy's Story
A Happy, Hopeful Place

My desire is to feel healthy in my body and to trust that I am going to find that place where I just step back and follow my intuition. And that's exactly what I'm doing.

In early 2018, Cindy, 51, began experiencing symptoms of diabetes. A size 24 at the time, she wanted to lose weight. However, her track record with dieting had always ended in disappointment. In fact, she was a self-proclaimed serial dieter. So this time, Cindy decided to use the teachings of Abraham-Hicks (since these teachings had improved so many other areas of her life) to help her get healthier.

"Other people have different journeys," says Cindy. "They like to chart their progress, and that's what keeps them motivated. I am motivated by savoring my life experiences and being thankful for the contrast that brought them. Trust is the word in my mind right now. I trusted the information I learned from Abraham-Hicks and my Inner Being and now I can look back six months and say, 'Wow, it was just so easy.' People often say, 'Oh, I know how hard it is to lose weight.' And I'm thinking, it hasn't been hard at all. It's literally been zero effort."

Cindy also decided what she wasn't going to do. She wasn't going to focus on weight-loss goals, and she wasn't going to take on yet another food plan that would make her feel restricted or deprived. Instead, she decided to put her attention on getting into alignment, raising her vibration and "chilling" on her back porch whenever possible. In her spare time, Cindy would grab a cup of herbal tea, listen to Abraham audios and then meditate. She would also write in her journal about all the things she could think of that she appreciated, including her six grown children and seven grandkids.

"I don't count calories," Cindy shares. I don't weigh myself. I don't measure myself. I still don't have a goal weight because I trust that my body will eventually find its happy place and just let me know, 'Okay, we're here now. This feels good, this is the size I'm happy with, the size I can easily maintain.'"

Through studying Abraham, Cindy knew that taking time to quiet her mind would lead her to feeling better about herself and her body. She believed that making her alignment a priority would guide her to what she should do next in terms of her health. This was her plan because she knew she wasn't going to make any headway toward a healthier body until she was in a happy, hopeful place, and alignment was the key to getting there. "You've got to learn to be intentional about your alignment or you're never going to get anything done," shares Cindy. "You're never going to get what you want if you don't practice alignment and allowing. If you can get yourself to hopefulness, you are getting close to your vortex, and the vortex will take you in. And so that's where I try to live my life—in that happy, hopeful place."

After about a month of journaling, meditating and listening to Abraham audios, Cindy had an inspiration. To her surprise, the inspiration guided her to join the YMCA. To her even bigger surprise, she was inspired to join the water aerobics class. As it turned out, she loved exercising in the water. Her body felt light, flexible and free. Soon after joining the YMCA, Cindy began to ponder specific food plans that might work for her—that didn't feel restrictive. She knew it wasn't necessary to adopt a plan, but she felt as though she wanted one that would be easy and fun. Nothing immediately jumped out at her, but she believed the answers would come. And they did. One day, Cindy noticed she felt inspired to jumpstart her new lifestyle with a 10-day veggie/smoothie detox that she had done several times before. She started on the detox, and about five days in, a strong craving for a particular food presented itself. So she went to Instagram, which she often does, and shared about her cravings. Long story short, someone recommended a certain food plan based on those cravings, and that food plan turned out to be a perfect match! It was an easy plan that brought Cindy both enjoyment and extreme success. She didn't feel restricted or deprived, and in just six months, she went down five sizes from a 24 to a size 14.

The beauty of Cindy's story is everything that happened was a kind of natural unfolding. She made getting into alignment her first priority, and from there came the guidance she began to trust and follow. Cindy says it best herself, "I learned that I didn't need to see all the steps. I just needed to see the next step in front of me and trust the process."

Cindy's 5 Steps

STEP 1
Breathe
This entails setting aside a bit of intentional time to meditate, appreciate and visualize until you find some calm.

STEP 2
Write
After you've found some calm, I suggest writing in a journal. I call mine my Joy Journal. I write about things that bring me joy, including lists of things I appreciate about a person, an experience or myself. I write a little bit or a lot, depending on the flow of ideas.

STEP 3
Trust
This is more in the realm of something I notice as it begins to happen. I notice that I am more easily trusting the Universe to hold my desires and guide me toward them.

STEP 4
Expect
This builds on trust and is again something I watch for and appreciate as it appears. I expect Source to inspire me with feasible ideas, and I also expect things to go well for me, including my weight-loss process.

STEP 5
Follow
This is simply following the good-feeling inspiration that comes.

Paula's Story
Write It, Speak It, Live It!

Throw all those limitations out the window and write your own story. Write it and speak it and dream it until you believe it. No one gets to write your story except you.

When Paula was 16, she injured her knee playing soccer. The doctors said she would never run or ski again and would need surgery to repair her knee to the extent that was even possible. This was devastating news to Paula, who lived in Okanagan, Canada, and loved athletics. She put the surgery on hold while working with her physical therapist, who held a slightly different opinion: "Why don't we see what your body can do? You are young and perhaps, with therapy, your knee will heal." The physical therapy worked and Paula, now 40, did in fact run and ski again and still does to this day. "That was an early lesson about the power of belief," says Paula, "although I didn't fully understand it at the time."

In college, Paula entered what she calls a "toxic-waste playground" phase. "I was quite self-destructive," she admits. "Drinking almost every night with my college friends was the norm. I was also in a dysfunctional relationship with a man where I pretty much gave my power away. I wasn't taking care of myself physically or emotionally, existed on junk food and gained 25 pounds. I developed digestive problems, including an ulcer and food sensitivities that made me bloated and lethargic. Constantly stressed out, I realized this was the age when I was supposed to be at my prime and yet there I was, feeling my absolute worst."

When Paula graduated, she knew it was time to make some changes. "I decided to take a year off from men, coffee, dairy, gluten and alcohol because I needed to heal my gastrointestinal tract and my psyche," says Paula. She was beginning a new path to feeling better physically and emotionally.

Soon after, one of her friends referred Paula to a psychic. A skeptical-but-intrigued Paula signed up for a reading at the metaphysical bookstore. The moment she walked in, the psychic grabbed the Abraham-Hicks book *Ask and It Is Given* from the bookshelf, walked up to Paula, held the book to her face and yelled, "You need to read this book!" Though Paula thought the woman's behavior a little bizarre, she managed to force a smile. They proceeded with the reading, which turned out to be extremely helpful to Paula. Before she left, the psychic wrote a few things down on a piece of paper, including four words, "The Law of Attraction."

Paula didn't purchase the Abraham-Hicks book that day, but she did return to the bookstore months later for another session with the psychic. As soon as she walked in, the psychic grabbed the same book from the bookshelf, walked up to Paula and yelled, "You need to read this book!" This time Paula replied, "I know."

She brought the book home and read it in two days. "*Ask and It Is Given* blew my mind," recalls Paula, who was 24 years old at the time. "After reading the book, I was incredibly excited, and it dawned on me that I could use the Law of Attraction to become healthier. I was still

struggling with some lingering digestive issues, and I also believed that if I could let go of the 25 pounds I gained in college, my body would be happier. The book has 22 processes to help you create what you want in your life, and I decided to start with Process #2: The Magical Creation Box."

"I found a large purple (my favorite color) gift box and wrote the words, 'Whatever is contained in this box—IS!' on the lid," Paula continues, "just like the instructions recommended. I put pictures and small representations of everything I truly desired in my life into the box. I included magazine photos of women with the body type I wanted along with pictures of women exercising and pictures of healthy foods. I added positive affirmations on little pieces of paper and phrases such as 'Fit at Every Age' and 'Time to Play.' I didn't put anything in the box about 'weight.' Everything in my Creation Box was about being healthy."

"I had been eating more nutritious foods for a while," Paula explains, "but when I decided to deliberately put the Law of Attraction to work for me, I really started to feel better physically. I believe it was that mental switch that set things in motion. As a wonderful side effect, I started to release two pounds a month. I'm 5'9" and was 160 pounds at the time. In a year, I let go of 24 pounds. I wasn't even trying and had never released weight that easily before!"

"The main thing I tell people is, don't let anything limit you," says Paula. "My doctors told me I would never ski or play soccer again, but my physical therapist helped me believe differently. I ski patrolled for three years, taking 200-pound men down double black diamond runs, snow plowing with them behind me. I also went wake boarding and was able to jump over the whole wake and land on the other side, which the doctors thought I would never be able to do. I think my knees got to the point where there was no limitation to my strength!"

I have been a lifeguard," Paula adds. "I rock-climbed. I played women's competitive soccer. I've gotten out of unhappy relationships and created healthy ones. I've built my own business and found the most incredible places to live. I still have small ups and downs, but I know what to do now. I know I get to choose alignment in each moment and create my life from there."

Paula's 5 Steps

STEP 1
Write Your Own Story

We've all been told things by well-meaning family, friends or teachers that wound up limiting us in some way. Maybe they said you couldn't act or sing or it wasn't in your genes to be a fast runner or a good artist. Maybe you were told that all the women in your family were big and that's just the way it is. I say, throw all those limitations out the window and write your own story. Write it and speak it and dream it until you believe it. No one gets to write your story except you.

STEP 2
Transform Your Inner Dialogue

I'm a physical therapist, and my patients often say things like, "I have a bad back." I'll reply, "Actually, you have a good back that needs some therapy," or "Your back is still holding you together," or "Your back has gone through a lot and needs some love." Many of us also criticize our appearance. I used to say things like, "I hate my hips and thighs," or "I hate my stomach." Start changing that language and instead say only positive things about your body to yourself and others.

STEP 3
Make a Magical Creation Box

This process is directly from *Ask and It Is Given* by Esther and Jerry Hicks. You start by choosing a box of your liking and begin to fill it with magazine clippings and other representations of all the things you want to manifest in your life. If you want to transform your body or your health, find pictures that represent your new body and add them. Once your items are in the box, consider it done—you don't have to keep thinking about it unless you want to. Add items to your Creation Box as often as you like. I love this process because you really get to see how you create your world with your thoughts.

STEP 4
Eat What Agrees with You

When you learn to listen to your body, you can easily find out what it likes and what it doesn't. Your body is constantly giving you clues, and eventually the clues get "louder." For instance, I developed an ulcer at a young age, and that was definitely stress-related so I had to find a way to decrease my stress. If your stomach gets inflamed and bloated after you eat gluten, that's a clue that maybe you shouldn't eat that. At the same time, you don't want to get caught in a guilt trap. Be forgiving and patient with yourself. Like everything else, listening to your body is a process.

STEP 5
Get Happy

Most of the time, we think we'll be happy when we achieve the things we want, but it's actually the other way around. We achieve the things we want when we get happy, and that includes creating the body we desire. It's very difficult to transform your body or your health when you are in a low vibration. People will often say, "How can I be happy about my health if I'm sick or happy about my weight when I want to be thin?" Learning how to be happy (or feel better) is actually the work. Once you start to make feeling emotionally good your number one priority, you will begin to see improvement.

Crystal's Story
Fake It Till You Make It

If you have spent many years hating your body and putting yourself down, or being around someone who puts you down, you need a giant mindset change—not a diet.

C rystal, now 39, reveals that she was in a marriage where her husband was emotionally abusive and regularly accused her of having affairs. He belittled her and tried to control her. During the same time, Crystal was unhappy with her job and her weight. She had promised herself she would never get up to 200 pounds again, but one morning when she got on the scale, the number read 202. "This was my low point," Crystal shares. "I remember bawling my eyes out in my car, talking to a stranger I met on Snapchat and telling them how I'd hit rock bottom. I couldn't stop sobbing. It wasn't just the weight, it was everything, including my husband and my job. It all came to a head. I finally looked around and the sun was still shining. It was an absolutely gorgeous day and somehow I mustered up the strength to say to myself, 'This is not the end of the world. You can totally turn this around.' I got out of my car and started walking on a nearby trail. I began to appreciate the nature all around me and realized how much I wanted to find a way to love my life."

From that point on, Crystal walked every day and started drinking lots of water. Those were two changes she could implement immediately. While her mood improved, she continued to struggle with her marriage, job and lack of self-esteem. A few weeks later, a friend recommended *aha*. "Watching that movie left me with a happy feeling," she recalls. "I felt hopeful for the first time in a long time. I finally had some answers."

That began Crystal's journey of learning about Abraham-Hicks and the Law of Attraction. She joined LOA and Abraham-Hicks groups online and began to ask questions such as, "How can you lose weight using the Law of Attraction?" "How can you build your self-esteem?" "How can you leave your marriage?"

Crystal started to implement the "Fake it till you make it" philosophy. Initially the idea seemed silly, but she decided to give it a try. "Every morning while taking a shower, I would tell my body how much I loved and appreciated it," she says. "I would tell it how I appreciate its five senses that allow me to see, hear, smell, taste and touch, and my other senses that allow me to connect with my Inner Being. I would tell it that I appreciate it for its amazing ability to heal itself. I started focusing on the things I could be thankful for right then, without looking in the mirror and reminding myself of my flaws. I basically began bringing in some positivity in relation to my body."

Next, Crystal made a decision to celebrate every victory, no matter how small. "Whether I lost an ounce or a pound, whether I walked one or five miles and whether I drank one or three liters of water, I turned everything into a positive," she explains. "I looked for things to celebrate. This accomplished two purposes: 1) It put me in a higher vibration, and 2) It motivated me to continue. I'm not saying I never got discouraged, but when that happened, I learned to talk myself into feeling better. I looked at the reason for my discouragement as a lesson instead of a failure because it was teaching me something."

"Appreciation and celebration put me in the mindset of loving and accepting my body in its current form," continues Crystal. "I had to accept myself as perfect the way I was before I was able to make changes. As Abraham points out, when I'm satisfied where I am, that puts me in the receiving mode to allow what I want to come into my life. If I'm dissatisfied with where I am and continue to criticize my body, I'm refusing to allow my new body to emerge."

"There is nothing wrong with me," says Crystal. "That's probably my biggest lesson. I am not defective. I am not unlovable. I am this wonderful, beautiful being with unlimited potential to expand and grow."

Once Crystal began to change her mindset, she noticed she was letting go of weight quickly. She explains how it was a domino effect because the more weight she released, the better she felt, and the better she felt, the more she was inspired to continue this path. "Once the ball was rolling, it was pretty easy to keep the momentum going," Crystal says. "I really didn't watch what I was eating, but I noticed that my appetite decreased and I craved healthier foods. I was also getting happier, so I didn't use food as an escape from depression anymore."

Crystal went on to release 66 pounds in 10 months, getting down to 136 and keeping it off for over four years now. She has since gotten a divorce and is happy in a new relationship. She also has a new job that she enjoys much more than the furniture store position.

"It's that positive momentum that keeps you attracting the body you want," concludes Crystal. "When you're appreciating and celebrating, you attract things you didn't even know were possible."

Crystal's 5 Steps

STEP 1
Inspired Action
Once you start focusing more positively on your body, yourself and your life, you will attract other thoughts that are more positive in nature. You will begin to get inspired to do things. Maybe you will be inspired to take a walk or to drink more water. Maybe you will be inspired to call a friend who tells you about a new food plan that winds up changing your life. Inspired action begins with trusting the inspiration you receive. If you're not receiving any inspiration right now, tell yourself to be patient because eventually it will come.

STEP 2
Accept Where You Are
Many people think that accepting is the same as settling. It is not. You have to know where you're starting. Imagine if you want to map a trip between two points. You must know where you're starting point is, right? You don't say, "I don't accept that starting point. I hate that starting point. That starting point is ugly." You accept where you are and know that you can move forward from there. You can't make changes to your body while focusing on hating your body as it is now. Your mind is focusing on what's wrong, and the Law of Attraction will give you more of what you're focused on: hating your body. When you accept your body as is, you are making peace with your starting point and beginning to move forward.

STEP 3
Appreciation

Appreciation is your best friend. You want to get really good at appreciating the smallest to the biggest of things because this alone will transform your life. I started appreciating the functionality of my body. That is the best I could do, as I was not in a place where I could appreciate the appearance of my body yet. So I focused on my five senses. I focused on my body's ability to heal. I focused on the few things I did like about my body's appearance. From there, my appreciation continued to grow. Today, I love my appearance. I think I am beautiful and sexy. I am unapologetically confident, and I love this feeling.

STEP 4
Mindset

It's easy to give up when you don't see quick results. Lots of diets help people let go of weight fast, but dieters usually gain the weight back just as fast. This approach is not a diet. It's about changing your entire mindset. If you have spent many years hating your body and putting yourself down, or being around someone who puts you down, you need a giant mindset change—not a diet. A diet doesn't address the way your mind works. It only addresses your food. Changing your mindset is a process, but when you're aware of the Law of Attraction, you know you're not doing this alone. You know miracles can happen, and you can totally transform your mind, your body and your life.

STEP 5
Momentum

This is my favorite step because as momentum builds, things start happening faster and faster and you begin to feel better and better. To get your momentum going toward letting go of pounds, all you have to do is practice the other steps. If you feel discouraged along the way, that's okay too. Just get back to thinking more positive thoughts about your body and your life as soon as you can. It's natural to have ups and downs. You've got to stop beating yourself up and get back to positive mindset practices. Forgive yourself as many times as it takes and let it go. The results are totally worth it.

Acknowledgments

This book started out as an inspiration from Source that I finally verbalized to my husband, Steve, during a walk around Lake Lily in Maitland, Florida, many years ago. As my rock and anchor, Steve has encouraged each dream, each business idea and each writing project, including this one. I want to thank him for his support during the development and writing of this book and for handling all the technical aspects. I'm so blessed to have him as my husband and business partner.

I want to thank Karen Money Williams for hosting Abraham-Hicks discussion groups in her home in Florida with her partner, Mark Toms. Those meetings changed my life and formed the impetus for a decade-plus long *(and still going strong)* study of Abraham-Hicks. I am proud to call Karen my friend, confidante and mentor as well as the editor and enthusiastic supporter of this book.

There are many other people I wish to thank including my first Abraham-Hicks Weight Loss coach, Diana. Her calming, light-hearted, common sense voice on the other end of the phone helped me learn how to relax about food (and life) for the first time in decades.

Other friends and family I would like to thank include Susan Marlan, Kathleen Forrest, Regina Zastrow, Austin Ryder (my son) and the members of my Delicious Alignment Facebook group. Your enthusiasm and loving support for this project *(and for me)* kept me from giving up whenever my feelings of "not being good enough, thin enough or worthy enough" took over.

I would also like to thank Julie Hale for her contributions to this book, my daughter, Amanda Ryder, for transcribing the interviews, and my biggest cheerleader, my father, Robert Ryder. His loving support has touched my heart more than he knows, and I am so grateful to have him in our lives.

In addition, I want to express my deep appreciation to the 25 women who shared their stories of spiritual and physical transformation with me. This book could not have been written without them.

Lastly, I want to thank Esther and Jerry Hicks for following their Inner Guidance and sharing Abraham with the world. I am so happy they did!

Resources

Visit my Resources page at DeliciousAlignment.com. There's no better way to keep the conversation (and the momentum) going than to surround yourself with like-minded people who understand your journey and who will cheer you on. On this site you will find a plethora of resources including social media links, individual and group programs as they become available, and more. Joining the Delicious Alignment community is a great way to empower yourself every day.

Made in the USA
Middletown, DE
14 May 2020